Oldbourne History of Science Library
Editor: Michael A. Hoskin

MEDICINE IN MEDIEVAL ENGLAND

Titles in the Oldbourne History of Science Library:

MEDICINE
IN MEDIEVAL
ENGLAND

C. H. TALBOT

This book is published and distributed
in the United States by
AMERICAN ELSEVIER PUBLISHING COMPANY, INC.
52 Vanderbilt Avenue, New York, N.Y. 10017

OLDBOURNE BOOK CO. LTD,
2 Portman Street, London W.1

© *Oldbourne Book Co. Ltd, 1967*

Set in Georgian and printed in Great Britain
by Purnell and Sons Ltd, Paulton (Somerset) and London

Contents

List of Plates

Preface

This book is addressed to the general reader, not to specialists; I cannot claim to say in it anything which is new or revolutionary, though it may redress the balance in certain generally-accepted attitudes. To add footnotes would have overloaded the pages to such an extent that the text would have suffered. But the reader can rest assured that the references exist and that nothing is said here which is not found in the original texts or in manuscripts.

Chapter One

Anglo-Saxon Medicine

The history of medicine in England may be said to begin with the Anglo-Saxon Leech-Books, and more precisely with the Leech-Book of Bald, which was written about the middle of the tenth century. This does not mean that in the previous centuries medicine was not known or practised, but simply that the evidence for it has disappeared. During the Roman occupation of Britain, it can be presumed that the highly civilised and highly organised society, with its cities, towns and camps, comparable to those on the mainland of Europe, included physicians, surgeons, oculists and other professional specialists to care for the health of the population. But few traces of their existence and activity remain. Apart from the temple settlement at Lydney in Gloucestershire, where the healing God Nodens was supposed to have effected cures, and a few sherds which indicate the presence of druggists, oculists, army surgeons and the like, other tangible and significant evidence has disappeared. Unlike France, Spain and Italy, which preserved some remnants of their classical connections, England can show few vestiges, apart from ruins, of its centuries of civilisation.

When the Saxons came to these shores, they made immediate contact, not with a Romanized society, but with the descendants of the serfs who had clustered in villages on the outskirts of the Roman cities. These it was, rather than the civilised inhabitants of the towns and villas, who were to shape the new society. Like all primitive peoples the Saxons had some knowledge of herbs and a rudimentary acquaintance with surgery. But it was more empirical than rational; overlaid with magic and superstition and rooted in folklore. This was to persist long after the introduction of what is called rational medicine.

The knowledge and practice of rational medicine was first brought by the Christian missionaries who reached England about the year 570 A.D; however, as their purpose was primarily religious, little emphasis could have been laid on this facet of their work. Moreover, the process of conversion from paganism to Christianity was interrupted by sudden and prolonged defections, when war, famine or epidemic provoked a reversion to the ancient temples, cults and superstitions. Nevertheless, during the period 570–670 A.D., momentous intellectual links were forged with Ireland and Gaul, teachers and books were imported, schools established and the cultural level of Lerins, Luxeuil, Lyons and many other places was set as a standard for the English people.

The occasion for new and unexpected influences on English education was the death in Rome of Wighard, Archbishop-elect of Canterbury. To fill the vacancy the Pope invited Hadrian, an African trained in Southern Italy, 'a great scholar in Greek and Latin'. But he declined the honour and recommended in his stead a Greek, named Theodore, 'learned in both sacred and secular literature, fluent in Greek and Latin'. Theodore was then sixty-six years of age, intellectually mature, a man of immense energy and organizing ability, and so steeped in his native traditions that it was feared he might introduce Greek customs into the budding English church. To counteract this, Hadrian was appointed his mentor, and instructed to accompany Theodore through Gaul where he knew, from two previous visits, many highly placed officials. How essentially Greek this combination appeared may be judged by the fact that both of them, on their arrival in Paris, were detained at the court by Ebrin, the royal chamberlain, 'who suspected they bore messages from the Emperor [of Constantinople] to the kings of Britain'. During their journey through Gaul, which lasted a year, they stayed at Marseilles, Arles, Paris, Sens and Meaux; when they reached England their acquaintance with Gaulish traditions, ecclesiastical, educational and monastic, was consequently far from superficial. All this knowledge and experience was passed on to the English.

One of the first actions was to establish a school at Canterbury, where all the liberal arts, besides theology and law, could be studied. We know that medicine was included in the curriculum, for St Aldhelm, a pupil there, mentioned it as one of the subjects studied alongside astronomy and arithmetic, whilst St John of Beverley, criticizing the action of a physician, said, 'I remember that Archbishop Theodore ... used to say that it was dangerous to bleed at a time when the light of the moon and the pull of the tides was increasing'. Taking Theodore's own origin and education into account, it must be inferred that the medical theory taught at Canterbury was predominantly Greek. What texts were used cannot be established; the only catalogue of books which might have afforded some information (Alcuin's eulogy on the library of York) omits any mention of medical texts.

We may perhaps discover what texts were available by examining the trend of medical writing during the preceding centuries. After the Galenic period the wealth of medical material produced by authors appears to have daunted students, who had neither the time nor the patience, and certainly not the expertise, to sift through the accumulated material. Even at Alexandria, medical teaching was confined to twenty books, sixteen of Galen and four of Hippocrates. As a result, the demand for compilations, which selected passages from approved writers and provided a complete conspectus of all branches of medicine, grew steadily. Among the Greek compilers the first was Oribasius of Pergamos (fourth century) who drew up for the Emperor Julian an abridgement of the works of Galen. When it was completed Oribasius amplified it with passages from other Greek writers and called it *Medical Collections*. This vast encyclopedia in seventy books covered all medical knowledge amassed up to that time on hygiene, therapy and surgery. Valuable as it was, it proved too unwieldy for the average practitioner. Some years later, therefore, at the request of his son, Eustathius, he summarized its contents into nine books, entitled *Synopsis*, omitting all the passages which dealt with surgery, anatomy and medical apparatus and preserving only those sections which would be useful to a physician living at some distance from great towns. But even this, addressed to professional doctors, did not meet everyone's needs; so, a third compilation called *Euporistes*, designed to instruct ordinary people in the countryside, was drawn up. It consisted of four books, in which the symptoms of various diseases and the medicines to be prescribed were listed. Here can be seen, within the lifetime of one man and in connection with one medical work, the gradual process of erosion which was characteristic of the early Christian centuries: first, the elimination of original writings by compilation, then the abridgement of the compilation, and finally the reduction of the abridgement to one small but practical section of it.

Both these smaller compilations of Oribasius found their way to the West and were translated into Latin at Ravenna during the sixth or seventh century. An early copy of this date survives from the scriptorium of the abbey at Fleury-sur-Loire.

Another compiler was Alexander of Tralles, brother to the architect of St Sophia in Constantinople. Unlike Oribasius, though he made extensive use of Galen, he added the fruits of his own experience gathered in travels through Italy, Gaul and Spain. Curious charms, superstitions and folk-medicine, possibly copied from Pseudo-Galen *De remediis parabilibus*, form part of his work, but most of them were eliminated from the seventh-century Latin translation of his book and were not transmitted to the West.

Alexander was followed by Paul of Aegina, the compiler of an epitome of medicine in seven books, almost half of which was filched from Oribasius without acknowledgement, the rest belonging to Galen with an occasional reference to Alexander. What appears to be original, prefaced with the words, 'I saw', 'I did', is often no more than a bare transcription of his source material. Like the original compilation of Oribasius, it was found by later ages to be too lengthy for complete translation and only the third book, rather late in the tenth century, found its way into Italy. The sixth book, dealing with surgery, had a different fate, with which we shall deal in another chapter.

There were, apart from these three main writers, two others, Aretaeus (first century) and Aetius of Amida (sixth century), the latter of whom compiled a medical encyclopedia, the *Tetrabiblos*: but neither of these had any influence on the West.

These, then, would have been the sources to which Theodore of Canterbury had access before he came to England at the end of the seventh century. Whether, in fact, he used or possessed them is a question that cannot be answered.

What of Hadrian, Theodore's companion? As has been said, he was African by birth, Italian by monastic training. His medical sources, supposing him to have been interested, would have been Latin compilations based essentially on the same Hippocratic and Galenic material, with additions from later Latin writers.

The most important Latin compilation of medicine was that of Celsus, whose purpose had been to create a vast encyclopedia of the arts, embracing agriculture, military techniques, rhetoric, philosophy, jurisprudence and medicine. Of this scheme only the medical section has survived. Celsus was not a practising physician and he engaged slaves well versed in the subject to collect his material for him. His work, remarkable for its completeness and symmetry, has been acclaimed as a wonderful text-book, particularly from the surgical point of view. But just as the bulk of the sections on agriculture, rhetoric, philosophy and jurisprudence militated against their survival, so the size of the eight books *De medicina* made it too costly for the ordinary practitioner. Few copies of it were made during the medieval period, and even the four manuscripts of it that survive (two of the ninth century, one of the tenth and another of the fifteenth, divided between Italy and France) appear to have attracted few, if any, readers. Consequently its influence on medieval medicine was minimal.

Far different was the fate of the work of Soranus of Ephesus who worked as a physician in Rome during the reigns of Trajan and Hadrian, that is, shortly before the time of Galen. A translation of this work entitled *De morbis acutis et chronicis libri VIII* was made sometime about the end of the fourth, or beginning of the fifth century, by Caelius Aurelianus, a native of Sicca in Numidia, North Africa. His work was recommended for study to the monks of Vivarium by Cassiodorus (487–583) in the following passage:

And so study with care the nature of herbs and the compounding of drugs. If you have no knowledge of Greek, you have at hand the

13

Herbarium of Dioscorides, who fully described the flowers of the fields and illustrated them with drawings. After that read Hippocrates and Galen in their Latin versions, Galen's treatise *Ad Glauconem* and the anonymous author who made a compilation from various writers. After that read Aurelius Caelius *De medicina*, Hippocrates *De herbis et cibis* and other books dealing with the art of medicine, all of which I have left to you on the shelves of the library.

This translation was in use at Lorsch during the ninth century, but whether it had greater diffusion is doubtful; the only copy disappeared after an edition had been made by Sichard in 1529. Caelius, however, wrote a work of his own based on Soranus, entitled *Medicinales responsiones libri III*, which was intended as an introduction to medicine under the form of question and answer, and from the first two books two compilations were formed with the titles *De salutaribus praeceptis* and *De diaeticis passionibus*. Both these were purely theoretical and included no remedies for the cure of disease. But from them were compiled two further treatises during the seventh century, one under the name of Aurelius, *De acutis passionibus*, and the other under the fictitious Aesculapius, *De chronicis passionibus*, both apparently from the same hand. These were designed as practical helps for the physician.

Somewhat later, Cassius Felix, also a native of Africa, produced in 447 A.D. his book *De medicina ex græcis logicae sectae autoribus liber translatus*, a compilation based principally on the writings, genuine and spurious, of Galen, with a section on gynaecology taken from Soranus. Copies of this treatise appear to have been rare and his name was scarcely mentioned until Simon Januensis examined the text in the thirteenth century for his list of medical synonyms.

On the purely medical side there were, besides, the authentic works of Hippocrates and Galen, but in small number. As the quotation from Cassiodorus shows, their works were known in Latin versions: these works were, for Hippocrates, the *De aere, aquis et locis, Prognosticon, De victus ratione, Aphorismi, De mulierum affectibus* and *De diaeta salubri*, though the versions of some of these stem from a later date than Cassiodorus; for Galen, *Ad Glauconem de medendi methodo, De sectis*, and *De simplicium medicamentorum temperamentis et facultatibus*. Whether at this time the pseudo-writings of both these authors, mostly extracts from their works, were available, is not clear.

In pharmacology the material was much more abundant. Here Pliny's *Historia naturalis* takes the lead, a work planned on the same gigantic proportions as Celsus' encyclopedia, but with less critical selection. The twelve books dealing with medicine are little more than a tissue of empirical remedies, containing all that was irrational and debased in Roman medicine. But it seems to have been overlooked that the sources from which most of this material was garnered were predominantly Greek and that Pliny quotes no fewer than fifty Greek physicians as his authorities, many of whom were later used by Galen.

Pliny's book was the source of other compilations, the most celebrated of which, the *Medicina Plinii*, drawn up in the fourth century, had an immense vogue in the Middle Ages. Like Pliny himself, the author of this work was not a practising physician but a layman, who addressed his book to ordinary folk dwelling far from the towns, who found it difficult or expensive to procure the customary medical remedies. It is a purely practical manual without a trace of medical theory. Like Pliny he arranged ailments from head to foot, a tradition that was to endure for centuries.

From Pliny also another compilation was abstracted by Marcellus of Bordeaux, a high-born official who wished to help his friends to avoid the exorbitant demands of physicians; he has certain elements in common with the *Medicina Plinii* and may have borrowed them from that source. Yet another compilation from the same fundamental material is the *Herbarium* of Pseudo-Apuleius, possibly drawn up at the end of the fifth century in North Africa, where Apuleius of Madaura enjoyed a great reputation for magic. It may be connected with the lost book *De expertis remediis* of Vindician (a contemporary and friend of St Augustine) which was quoted by two other African writers, Theodorus Priscianus and his pupil Cassius Felix.

The chief work, however, on pharmacology was that of Dioscorides, a native of Tarsus in Cilicia. The original text consisted of five books dealing with spices, salves and oils, then with parts of animals and animal products, then with plants and roots, and finally with wines and minerals. At an early period the book was adapted for easier use by arranging it in alphabetical order and illustrating it with pictures, probably taken from the work of Crateuas. A medieval Latin version of it, with the title *Herbarium Dioscoridis*, was known to Cassiodorus in the sixth century and the title implies that it was limited to medicinal plants: it bears the same relation to the genuine Dioscorides as the *Medicina Plinii* to the *Natural History* of Pliny.

There was, then, a fairly extensive medical literature available at the time Theodore and Hadrian were teaching at Canterbury, consisting of translations from the Greek, works originally written in Latin, and compilations made from both Greek and Latin. We can only surmise what actually was used, for no writer of this period, English or Irish, mentions any medical book by title. We know for certain that Bede had a copy (though not complete) of Pliny's *Historia naturalis*; he had a good text of Cassius Felix, as is proved by his quotation of the entire chapter forty-eight on dysentery in his *Retractations*; he had access to the Pseudo-Hippocratic treatise on regimen ascribed by Paul of Aegina to Diocles. A text either of Dioscorides or of Pseudo-Apuleius must have been in the possession of Cynehard, Bishop of Winchester, for he wrote to Lull at Mainz asking him to procure books on medicine, because those he already had only contained the names of foreign drugs. Another letter addressed to a correspondent in Germany asked for books on the natural sciences.

But our judgement on these matters is necessarily based on surmise. We know that before the Danish invasions destroyed the monasteries and the libraries in England there was constant intercourse between this country and the continent. Willibrord, the missionary of the Frisians, founded Echternach, to which many Englishmen afterwards repaired; Boniface, the Apostle of Germany, founded Fulda, the educational centre from which other abbeys, like Reichenau, took their rise; and between these and English monastic establishments books passed to and fro. Even St Gall in Switzerland, originally an Irish foundation, housed many Englishmen. That exchanges of texts between monks and clerics took place is clear not only from Boniface's correspondence, from the surviving books at Wurzburg and the survival of the Codex Amiatinus at Florence, but also from the fact that at his death at Beneventum, Hunwine was carrying books with him. The libraries at Wearmouth and Jarrow had originally been built up by purchases of manuscripts abroad and Aldhelm at Malmesbury is known to have travelled to Dover to buy books from merchants trading across the Channel. The outstanding example is that of Lupus of Ferrières who borrowed from York texts which he was unable to find in the whole Frankish kingdom.

After the Danish invasions conditions were otherwise; the monasteries were destroyed, the libraries dispersed and learning suffered a tremendous setback. Towards the end of the ninth century, Alfred remarked in the preface to his translation of St Gregory's *Regula pastoralis*: 'So completely had learning decayed in England that there were few men on this side of the Humber who could learn their services in English, or even translate a letter from Latin into English . . . I cannot recollect a single man south of the Thames who could do this when I succeeded to the Kingdom.' There may be a degree of exaggeration in this description; but the situation was soon remedied.

Grimbald, a monk of St Bertin, was sent over by Fulk, Archbishop of Rheims; John, the Saxon, came over from Corvei; Asser came from Wales, and there were others like Plegmund (later Archbishop of Canterbury), Werferth, Bishop of Worcester, and Athelstan and Werwulf, priests, who came from Mercia. Contact with Ireland was also renewed, for three scholars, Dubslane, Maccbethu and Maelinum, came to Alfred's court to report the death of Swifneh, 'the best teacher among the Irish'. From this time intellectual life flourished again. Alfred's enterprise in translating Latin works into English was spurred on by the knowledge that 'many could read things written in English' and his example was followed by others. From the early ninth century onwards an increasing use of the vernacular is evident and the rapid multiplication of copies of the Chronicle and the old English Martyrology suggests not only that literacy was widespread, but that English was superseding Latin in some fields.

It is precisely at this point that we find the earliest Leech-Books. The first of these, the Leech-Book of Bald, so-called from the colophon at the end of the first part, is believed to have been written between 900 and 950 A.D. The text that survives was not the first exemplar, but a beautifully finished copy of some text that already existed in Anglo-Saxon, so that we may date the Latin text, of which it is a translation, to a period somewhat earlier.

Among medical historians it has become popular to decry the value of this text. Whilst all are ready to subscribe to the view that a later Anglo-Saxon text, the *Peri Didaxeon*, is a partial translation of the work ascribed to Petrocellus (mistakenly accepted as a Salernitan), and is therefore more rational in its medical teaching, few seem to realise that the Leech-Book of Bald, written more than a century earlier, has more than forty passages from the same source. This is a discovery of the highest importance for the assessment of medical knowledge in England during the ninth and tenth centuries. What has to be insisted upon is that the Leech-Book is not barbarous, full of folk-lore, charms, incantations and the like; such a judgement could be passed only by those who have never read it attentively. The Leech-Book embodies the teaching of Greek writers as transmitted by Latin translations. There are in it long passages from Paul of Aegina, himself a compiler from Galen and other Greek authorities; there are extensive borrowings from Alexander of Tralles, and, more specifically, passages dealing with the spleen taken from Philagrios (a noted authority on this topic) and copied into the work of Alexander. There is a most interesting description of a surgical operation on the liver, the source of which has puzzled all writers up to the present time, but which is actually a text from Antyllus, one of the most celebrated surgeons praised by Galen. This particular passage, one of the few fragments of Antyllus which have survived, was incorporated by Oribasius into his *Medical Collections*: from him it passed to Petrocellus and from Petrocellus to the Anglo-Saxons. Besides these passages, we find large sections translated from the so-called Petrocellus, which is based on Cassius Felix and the Aesculapius-Aurelius complex, itself derived from Caelius Aurelianus, whose teaching is derived from Soranus. In short, far from the Leech-Book being a tissue of folk remedies and irrational ideas, it embodies some of the best medical literature available to the West at that time. Those who decry it base their remarks, not on rational analysis, but on ignorance. If, for instance, one compares the passage on the liver operation with the corresponding text in Celsus (acclaimed a 'rational' writer) the Leech-Book will be found to be fuller and better. If the treatment prescribed for the spleen, stomach and other organs in the Anglo-Saxon book is placed side by side with that of Celsus, it will be found more rewarding and informative. Indeed, even the irrational remedies which appear from time to time in the Leech-Book are the same as those used by Galen and Celsus. What is even more interesting, in view of derogatory remarks that have been made about the Anglo-Saxon copyists, is that the material has been reorganized and put into a more logical order, a result not of 'monastic stupidity' or even of 'scribal accident', but of a deliberate purpose pursued rationally.

In the Leech-Book a section containing forty-one 'crafts', and therefore quite extensive, was devoted to gynaecology. Though the chapter headings have survived, the text has been lost. But it raises an important question. In none of the compilations available to the Anglo-Saxons, except for a few chapters at the end of Cassius Felix, was there any comparable material. The matters dealt with were: obstruction of the naturalia, sterility, miscarriage, retention of urine, retention of secundinae, haemorrhage, mental unbalance, enlargement of the womb, hysterical aphonia, and various other women's diseases. The question arises as to where the Anglo-Saxons procured this part of their text. The only manuscript of approximately the same date and containing identical material is an abridgement of Hippocrates, *De mulierum affectibus*, now preserved in Leningrad, but originally belonging to the abbey of Corbie. It contains five other fragments based on Vindician, Muscio, Theodorus Priscianus and Pseudo-Theodorus. Another manuscript of the same treatise, but of the eleventh century and preserved in the British Museum, can be shown both by its orthography and format to derive from an 'Insular' source. Not only is there mention in it of an abbot from Northern Ireland (*Scotia*), of John Scotus Eriugena and Fergus 'the grammarian' who were together at Laon about 850 A.D., but also of Pardulus, Bishop of Laon, in 853 A.D. Is it pure coincidence that an amulet to bring about an easy birth, bearing the words 'Panditur interea domus Olimpi', derived from a seventh-century translation of Oribasius preserved at Laon, should be found in this manuscript and in the Leech-Book?

The probabilities are that the Hippocratic treatise was to be found in these islands, and the other fragments occurring in other Anglo-Saxon manuscripts dealing with the formation of the foetus, the signs of pregnancy, the prognostication of the sex of the child and other details of gynaecological interest, conform to the material available in the fragments that surround the original Hippocratic text.

Had not the Leech-Book survived, the later text, *Peri Didaxeon*, would have been considered the sole representative of what is called 'rational' medicine. We now know that it is a different translation of the same fundamental text, though the sections chosen do not tally with those of the Leech-Book. Furthermore, the earlier translator was superior. But the *Peri Didaxeon* provides one passage that the Leech-Book omitted, the introductory paragraphs on the history of medicine. This introduction has been derided as nonsensical. Yet, in fact, it is extremely valuable and instructive. It is a translation of a gloss on the *De sectis* of Galen, probably made at Alexandria in the sixth century, and intended as an introduction to the study of medicine: it is a unique fragment illustrating the teaching methods employed at the most celebrated medical centre of ancient times.

Besides the Leech-Books there were Anglo-Saxon translations of the *Herbarium* of Pseudo-Apuleius, made about 950 A.D, parts of Dioscorides and several other herbal texts, all beautifully illustrated. It must not be concluded that these were the first texts to appear in England, for the *Codex Hertensis 192,* of English origin, dating from the ninth century and containing Dioscorides, Antonius Musa and the work of Sextus Placitus, is earlier. Moreover, its text derives from another manuscript tradition, showing that several copies from different sources were extant. The illustrations to these texts are formal rather than natural, and it has been inferred that those who relied on them could not really distinguish or recognize any of the plants described; one might argue equally well that the Anglo-Saxons could not recognize, from the formalized illustrations of buildings, either a church or a monastery. What the illustrators tried to do was to impart to students the powers, the qualities and the effects of such plants.

Attached to these herbal texts was a small treatise written by an unknown Sextus Placitus Papyriensis, *Medicina de quadrupedibus,* and another *De taxone,* in the form of a letter sent by Idpartus, King of the Egyptians, to the Emperor Augustus. These works have been called 'disgusting' and 'nauseating'. The remedies, it is true, are not such as we use today; but they have their parallels in Greek and Roman medicine. Indeed, many of them are taken from Galen, his contemporaries and predecessors. A glance at Galen's writings will show that he was not averse to recommending burnt frogs, burnt mice, burnt ants, burnt hedgehog's head, burnt flies' heads, cat's droppings, dog's, camel's, ox's urine, frog's blood, snake's slough, and other animal products: and the names of the physicians connected with them are invariably Greek, such as Archigenes, Aesclepiades, Charicles, Nicomedes, Crito, Hierophilus, Xenocrates, Harpocrates and so on. When one considers that many of these confections were used as cosmetics, some even as dentifrice, and this during the classical period of medicine, it should come as no surprise that the Anglo-Saxons accepted them as stamped with supreme authority. Galen himself, when prescribing them, had said that he did not repudiate such folk medicine 'for by combining such experience with reason, we have an absolute and rational art'.

If we do not concern ourselves here with magic, contained for the most part in the *Lacnunga,* a text later than the Leech-Books and not so much a treatise on medicine as a commonplace-book, it is because it has been dealt with adequately, if not excessively, by those whose intention has been to denigrate Anglo-Saxon medicine. Suffice it to say that it is not typical of the culture of the period. That certain pagan elements are discernible in it should surprise no one acquainted with the history of the times. The Danes and

Norsemen who invaded England in the ninth century were not immediately converted to Christianity; indeed, parts of the country were completely pagan until well into the tenth century. In 926 a charter of Athelstan refers to the 'pagans' in Derbyshire as well as Bedfordshire, whilst even in 942 the boroughs of Leicester, Lincoln, Nottingham, Stamford and Derby were being described as 'rescued from the pagan Norsemen'. In Bede's time the kind of nonsense that appears in the _Lacnunga_ was not tolerated and even when he translated from the Greek a treatise dealing with the prognostications from the winds, and which merely concerned the weather, he was fearful that he might be accused of practising magical arts. The real attitude of Churchmen towards medicine can best be seen in the section devoted to medicine in Isidore's _Etymologies_, a work second only to the Bible in popularity during the Middle Ages. In not one instance does he counsel recourse to religious, superstitious or magical means for the treatment of disease. The healing of disease, he said, was not to be despised; it was of three kinds, pharmaceutical, surgical and dietetic. Diet consists in observing the laws of life, pharmacy consists in the use of medicaments, whilst surgery relies on incisions made by iron instruments. Whereas in ancient times medicine had consisted entirely of herbs and juices, modern methods of treatment included the administration of antidotes, pills, unguents, electuaries, poultices and plasters; surgery employed various instruments (which he described), and all these means could be learned from books. He ended by saying: 'Some will ask why the art of medicine is not included among the liberal arts? It is because they embrace individual subjects, whereas medicine embraces them all.' Medicine is called a second philosophy, because just as philosophy cures the soul, so medicine cures the body.

This was a commonsense attitude. No amount of quotations from the lives of saints, where miraculous cures are described, can obscure the fact that in a society which produced writers like Aelfric, Aethelweard (the Wessex elderman who wrote a chronicle in Latin), Wulfstan, Bishop of London, Byrhtferth and others, superstition and magic would have little place. It should be borne in mind that the few vernacular manuscripts that survive from this period are a minimal proportion of what actually existed. Historians are at pains to point out that manuscripts of this type had very little chance of survival. Subsequent changes in language, spelling, and script made them less valued by the generations that followed the tenth-century revival, when new influences from Fleury, Ghent and other cultural centres on the Continent brought in a flourishing era of Latin scholarship. They would have even less chance under the Normans, who through their ignorance of Anglo-Saxon caused everything to be translated for them into Latin. To lay great emphasis, then, on a single extravagant text like the *Lacnunga* is to throw everything out of perspective.

The *Lacnunga* is a rambling collection of about two hundred prescriptions, remedies, and charms derived from many sources, Greek, Roman, Byzantine, Celtic and Teutonic; it is a whole world apart from the scientific work of Byrhtferth, the monk of Ramsey. In 986 Abbo of Fleury accepted an invitation from Dunstan, Archbishop of Canterbury, and Oswald, Archbishop of York, to come to England, and he settled at Ramsey. There he taught the monks, among whom was Byrhtferth; he wrote for them a supplement to his treatise on astronomy, a short work on fractions, another on grammar and several other didactic and scientific tracts. He also promised to compose for Dunstan a treatise which the archbishop had been unable to extract from 'the teacher of Greek in his city'. The result of Abbo's activity was seen later in Byrhtferth's *Manual*, a book of instruction for young students on astronomy, mathematics, signs of the zodiac and calculations for drawing up the calendar with many other cognate subjects, in short, a handbook of elementary science, second only in importance to Bede's scientific works. It is this book, and not the farrago of superstitions and incantations, which is characteristic of the tenth century; and it is Byrhtferth, the foreign scholars from abroad, and their successors from Lotharingia and Lorraine, who rightly represent the true attitude towards science (and with it, medicine) current in England after the tenth-century revival. The *Lacnunga* may show 'the final pathological disintegration of Greek medical thought', but it does not show that Anglo-Saxon scholars were involved in it.

Chapter Two

Arab Medicine

About the time that St Augustine landed on the shores of Kent to spread Christianity, Mahomet was born, the great spiritual leader and creator of Islam. By the year 670, when Theodore and Hadrian founded their school of studies at Canterbury, the Arabs had conquered most of the Middle East; and by the time Bede was writing at Jarrow they had become firmly rooted in the South of Spain. The period of the Danish invasions in England, when the treasures accumulated during the previous two centuries were being wantonly destroyed, coincided with the prosperity of the Abbasides, Al-Mansur (754–775), Harun-al-Raschid (786–802) and Calif al-Mamun (813–833), under whom an enormous collection of Greek works was gathered together at Bagdad. Here, at the 'House of Wisdom' where the manuscripts were stored, a school of translators was established, so that all the important scientific writers of antiquity, Hippocrates, Dioscorides, Archigenes, Rufus of Ephesus, Galen, Oribasius, Philagrios, Alexander of Tralles and Paul of Aegina, were made available in Arabic translations.

The translators were for the most part Syrians, descendants of Nestorian heretics who had been driven from Constantinople two centuries earlier, but there were also Persians, Greeks and Jews, who all contributed to the diffusion of Greek science and literature. The earliest Syriac translations, mostly of Galen, had been made in the sixth century and for the use of Christians; but these versions were faulty and incomplete. When they were translated from Syriac into Arabic about the beginning of the ninth century the errors and misunderstandings increased and it was found necessary to undertake a complete revision. This work was entrusted to Hunain and his disciples, who, by collating the texts with original Greek manuscripts and employing scientific methods of criticism, were able to produce versions that were not only accurate but literary. At that time the traditional methods of the Alexandrian medical school were fully alive and the Arab school of medicine attached to the 'House of Wisdom' at Bagdad was modelled on them. Hunain tells us that the late Alexandrians limited their study of Galen to twenty books. Galen himself had wished that after his *De sectis* his anatomical works should be read first: so they compiled one treatise from his five books on anatomy of the bones, muscles, blood-vessels and nerves, and called it *On anatomy for beginners*. After that they studied his physiological works, then his books on diagnosis and prognosis, followed by his books on the treatment of disease, in particular the *Methodus medendi*. Later, the Arabs modified this programme to twelve books (and eventually four) of Hippocrates and sixteen of Galen, but it can be seen that in the ninth and tenth centuries a real knowledge of Hippocrates and Galen existed. During Hunain's period no less than 129 works of Galen, authentic and spurious, were known, and it was to provide an introduction to the study of these that he composed his famous *Isagoge*, which served as a text book of medicine throughout the Middle Ages.

By the middle of the tenth century, when the Anglo-Saxon Leech-Books first appeared and when a renaissance in the study of medicine was taking place at Chartres, the Arabs had reached the height of their power. The period of frenzied translation had passed, Greek science had been assimilated, and the Arabs were beginning to produce writings of their own. Their literary creativeness was phenomenal and the number of works produced ran into thousands. Not that all the 'books' which are attributed to certain authors would nowadays be considered as individual compositions, for many of them are no more than chapters from larger works presented separately. Their output, however, was sufficiently great to fill vast libraries, one of which, at Cordoba, had at least six hundred thousand volumes with a catalogue covering forty-four volumes. Not all of this work was original, at least in the field of medicine: much of it was mere commentary or a re-hash of Hippocratic and Galenic theory learned in translation, and the further removed the writers were from the early translations, the more they relied on compilations and abridgements of compilations. All the same, it had its value.

One of the most important of the Arab writers was Rhases, born, according to al-Bairuni, at Ray in northern Persia on 27 August, 865. He took up the study of medicine rather late after he had become proficient in philology, mathematics, philosophy and music. It has been said that his teacher was al-Tabari, but this cannot be true since al-Tabari died before Rhases was born. Nor is it true that he was asked to choose a site for the hospital in Bagdad, since this hospital was not founded until fifty years after his death; the hospital of which he took charge was Muqtadiriri, founded in 918 by order of the Caliph Muqtadir Bi'llah, who ruled from 908 to 932. Of the two hundred works attributed to him the only ones to have any influence on the West were his enormous encyclopedia *al-Hawi*, or *Continens*, and a shorter work entitled *Almansor*, so-called from the name of the Governor of Chorassan to whom it was dedicated. The *Continens* comprised twenty-four volumes, mainly a compilation of extracts from several hundred partly known or completely forgotten writers (whose works are now lost) and from Greek authors whose texts are available only in late Byzantine manuscripts. It covered the whole range of medical literature, enriched with his notes and comments and with records of cases taken from his own practice. Its purpose was to provide him with the material for writing a comprehensive book on medicine, but as he died before this could be accomplished, it was placed in the hands of his students to edit. The result is an ill-digested, badly arranged, wandering compilation resembling more a common-place book than a methodical treatise. Its bulk was so excessive that at certain periods no more than two copies could be found in the whole Mahomedan world and today there is no complete Arabic copy in existence: of the twenty-four original volumes no more than twelve, widely dispersed, survive.

Rhases was not only the pioneer in Arab medicine: he was also the nearest in spirit to Hippocrates. Though in theory he was a Galenist, his method was that of the Coan school, laying emphasis on hygienic and dietetic measures and employing simple drugs. 'Where a cure can be obtained by diet,' he said, 'use no drugs, and avoid complex remedies when simple ones will suffice.' His descriptions of diseases are accurate, based on clinical observation: his treatment was always directed by experience. His notes describe cases of renal abscess, dysentery, otitis followed by meningitis, aortic regurgitation, genital herpes, purulent conjunctivitis, appendicitis, mastitis, epilepsy. In one of his cases concerned with abortion, when surgery was required three times, it transpires that he did not treat the patient himself, but gave instructions to a midwife, who carried them out. Indeed, he had not examined the patient at all, but had to rely for his knowledge of the case on descriptions given by the patient's husband. This is revealing in view of Albucasis' claim to have treated many gynaecological cases. Rhases' patients came from all walks of life: his notes record treatment given to coppersmiths, booksellers, caravan guides, money changers, accountants, doorkeepers and tailors besides the higher officials and even Caliphs, so that it is obvious that he accepted patients without regard for their social or financial status.

He continually quotes his experiences in hospitals and shows how he questioned patients about their symptoms to gain information. He never approached sickness with preconceived ideas, and tested the theories of Hippocrates and Galen by recourse to experiments. To discover whether mercury could be prescribed without danger for some ailments, he even tried it out on his pet monkey and recognized from the animal's twisting, clawing and biting movements that it was an irritant and probably a poison.

He was vehement in his denunciations of charlatans and quacks. He portrayed them as practising every trick to deceive, pretending to cure epilepsy, to extract worms from the teeth and ears, to excise ranula from beneath the tongue, to cure haemorrhoids, and so on. His advice to people on choosing their physician was full of good sense: the physician should be a man of study, not one who had wasted his time singing, playing musical instruments and indulging in drink; he should be, besides learned in his profession, clever and shrewd, not argumentative or loquacious; he should have practised in large cities where he had gained wide experience through dealing with a variety of diseases 'for it is impossible for one man, even during a long life, to gain a complete knowledge of medicine, without following in the paths of his predecessors'. Though Rhases had complete confidence in his own experience, free as it was of superstition and rigid theory, he never contradicted the opinions of other doctors (who were evidently grouped into *sects*), but simply stated his own position without conceit or complacency. At times he recorded folk beliefs: for instance, he said that if a viper looked at an emerald, its eyes would liquefy, and so this stone was a prophylactic against poison: or that frogs pressed to decayed teeth would make them fall out. But these occasions were rare. His ideas on hygiene in the house were admirable and he described excellent methods for clearing the house of flies and vermin. Most of what he said can, naturally, be traced to earlier writers like Galen, Oribasius and Paul of Aegina, so that his teaching, when brought to the West by the translation of Gerard of Cremona in the middle of the twelfth century, did not materially alter the sum of medical knowledge. But his attitude, free of fixed theories, full of common sense, simple, and adaptable to various circumstances, without any disposition towards quackery, was an influence for good.

About a half-century after Rhases, Haly Abbas, born in southwest Persia, being dissatisfied with all previous books on medicine, decided to write his own. In his opinion Hippocrates was too brief; Galen too prolix and too inclined to waste words by arguing against his opponents; Oribasius' *Medical Collections*, except for one section, *De expilatione viscerum*, was no longer extant, whilst the *Synopsis* and *Euporistes* were deficient through omitting all reference to elements, complexions, humours, qualities, actions of the spirits, and so on; moreover, neither of them dealt with surgery. He levelled the same criticisms against Paul of Aegina, who, though he had devoted one section to surgery, had compiled his book without order and method. In the same way, Haly dismissed Ahrun, Mesue and John Serapion. The only man he praised was Rhases. But he also criticized the *Continens* as being a rambling affair devoid of proper arrangement into books, chapters and sections, frustrating to the reader and so voluminous 'that all, except a very few, despair of transcribing it'. Haly Abbas therefore decided to compile the perfect text-book. Anyone who studied it, he said, would need no other, for it contained everything essential for both learner and expert. All the same, the student ought to be proficient in logic, arithmetic, geometry, astronomy and music: logic, to understand the meaning of words; geometry, to know how to treat different forms of wounds (square, round and triangular); astronomy, to be able to prescribe medicines (because the moon and planets affect their qualities); music, to recognize the rhythm of the pulse. He divided his book into two main parts, one dealing with theory, the other with practice, each part containing ten books.

Though it is obvious that Haly Abbas had done little except systematize the teachings of his predecessors, he rarely quoted anyone but Hippocrates, Galen and Aristotle by name. His main sources were the *Aphorisms, De epidemia, De aere, aquis et locis* of Hippocrates, the writings of Galen, and those of Rhases, from whom he has taken large sections almost word for word. Unless one was aware of his sources, one would not know it was a compilation, so skilfully has he woven all the elements together. A comparison of his doctrine with that of his tenth-century contemporaries in the West shows that the essential content does not differ greatly. So, for instance, if one examines the chapters on the liver and the spleen in both Eastern and Western texts, they will be found to be in basic agreement. But whereas these subjects were dealt with in a single chapter in the West, Haly has one chapter dealing with the anatomy, another concerning the diseases, and a third in the *Practica* outlining the methods of treatment. It was this which made his book so much more logical, intelligible and practical.

Not only does Haly Abbas rely on earlier sources for his descriptions of diseases, but he takes over the medicines from them; frequently these are the same remedies as those used in Anglo-Saxon England. A typical instance is the following remedy for quinsy. The Leech-Book says: 'If thou find a white thost (dung) of a hound, dry it and rub it and sift it, and hold it against the swerecloth, and when need be mingle it with honey, smear the neck with it. . . . The hound must gnaw a bone ere he droppeth the thost, then will the thost be white and mickle.' This remedy has been classed by some writers as irrational, nauseating and disgusting. But the same remedy has its source in Galen; was taken over by Alexander of Tralles, then by Paul of Aegina; transferred unchanged to Haly Abbas; and then passed to Avicenna. The same borrowing of ideas regarding hygiene and dietetics can be traced equally clearly.

Though he criticizes his predecessors for not dealing with surgery, his own contribution is extremely meagre; it consists almost exclusively of cautery and scarification. He recommended the student to frequent places where several surgeons were known to operate: he was to watch carefully, learn the rules and examine their method of execution. Then he should practise under the supervision of a skilled operator and further his knowledge by study of books. The source of Haly's teaching on surgery is undoubtedly the sixth book of Paul of Aegina: all he has done is to abridge it, put it into better order, make it uniform and add passages from other Arab writers. Its importance for the Middle Ages lies in the fact that it preceded Albucasis and the work of the Salernitan, Roger Frugardi. It did not, however, contribute to the progress of surgery either in the evolution of thought or of technique. Its total dependence on older writers had the effect of holding back progress, not merely because it repeated what had been written centuries earlier, but also because in remodelling earlier material it used excessive brevity, resulting in lack of clarity and diminished utility. But in an age when so much had been destroyed the mere salvaging of knowledge became valuable, and so Haly's coordinated summary is a landmark in Arab medicine.

Haly's work exerted a great influence on the West. It was first translated by Constantine in the eleventh century. Owing, however, to the incompleteness of the translation, which omitted the whole of the *Practica*, with the exception of the ninth book, it was translated again by Stephen of Antioch, who finished the ten books of theory on 7 October, 1127, and the final ten books on practice on 3 January, 1128.

Just as the *Continens* of Rhases was superseded by the *Al-Maleki* of Haly Abbas, so in its turn it was supplanted by Avicenna's *Canon*.

Avicenna was born about 980 A.D. in Chorassan and brought as a child to Bokhara where his father was a high official. He was a child prodigy: at the age of ten he memorized the Koran; at twelve he disputed in logic and law; before he was sixteen he had read through the *Metaphysics* of Aristotle forty times; at seventeen he cured the Emir Nuch ben Mansur of a serious illness, and as a result was allowed free access to the royal library. After the death of his father he wandered from place to place, staying at the courts of Persian princes where he acted as statesman, physician, astronomer, teacher, author, finally being appointed vizier at Hamadan. When he fell under suspicion of treason, he fled to Isfahan, and eventually reached Ray, the birthplace of Rhases. There he spent fourteen years preparing his medical and philosophical masterpieces. Amidst the turmoil of government administration and excessive indulgence he composed his famous *Canon*, one of the most influential text-books ever written.

The exaggerated esteem in which he has been held by both contemporaries and successors is founded neither upon epoch-making discoveries nor upon his practical achievements, but rather upon his facility for assimilating facts and building them into a system. His work is an exposition of Galenism down to the smallest detail, worked out according to strict Aristotelian principles. His purpose appears to have been to establish medical thought and practice on an apparently immutable basis, so that what Galen did for Roman medicine, Avicenna did for Arab medicine. The immediate and lasting success of his work was due not to any originality of thought, but to its lucid diction, well-knit arrangement and logical procedure. Whereas Rhases had produced an armoury of disparate texts without order or analysis, and Haly Abbas had written a comprehensive textbook devoid of theory, Avicenna created a harmonious, orderly, comprehensive and rigidly logical system. His book was the final codification of Graeco-Arabic medicine, so closely interwoven that no single item could be subtracted without damaging the whole. To contemporary medical science it gave the appearance of almost mathematical accuracy and this it was that made the medieval world regard the *Canon* as an oracle from which it was impossible to dissent.

31

Had the original case records of Avicenna survived, which were intended to be an appendix to his system, some counterpoise might have existed to his excessive systematisation and theory and helped to readjust our judgement on his work. But as it was, the teaching of the *Canon* acted as a deterrent on unprejudiced observation and hindered research. The clinical approach, initiated and fostered by Rhases, had begun to languish under Haly Abbas, but under Avicenna it died a quick death. Moreover, the comprehensiveness of the *Canon* made recourse to ancient literature superfluous in an age when texts were expensive and laborious to copy. Thus it gave rise, not to independent and original works on medicine, but to smaller compilations from itself, to commentaries on certain sections of it, so that it led to an impoverishment, rather than an enrichment of medical science. For each work produced was but a faint reflection of Avicenna, who himself was but a compiler and commentator.

Avicenna was the last of the Persian trio of physicians: after his time the intellectual axis of Islam moved to the West, where Spain produced Albucasis, Avenzoar, Averroes and Maimonides.

Albucasis is chiefly remembered for his work on surgery, though it formed only one thirtieth of his medical system, *al-Tasrif*. He stands out as a solitary figure; for though Haly Abbas had dealt with surgery in his *al-Maleki*, his treatment was cursory and impersonal, whilst Albucasis (though deriving his ideas and practice from Paul of Aegina, and through him from Celsus) peppered his text with personal observations and critical digressions. His purpose was to promote new interest in a branch of medicine which, he complained, had almost disappeared from the Arab world; only in the writings of the ancients was there any reference to surgery, but because of bad translations, errors and alterations of the texts, the ideas were mostly unintelligible and useless. As a result, surgery was in the hands of charlatans, many of whom, through sheer incompetence, killed more patients than they healed.

Albucasis' book, illustrated with drawings of the instruments he used, provides a revealing glimpse of the high standard he set himself. He preferred, however, the branding iron to all other surgical instruments and he mentions more than fifty diseases which he personally treated with fire. Though he was perfectly aware that haemorrhage could be stopped by the use of styptics, ligature and complete division, cauterisation was the method he favoured. On the other hand he dealt with gynaecological matters at great length and in much detail, an adventurous enterprise considering the religious and ethical attitude of Islam to women. But it may be, as in the case of Rhases and Haly Abbas, that the examination of women, their treatment and even surgical operations may have been left to midwives to carry out under his instruction.

Albucasis is remembered also for his contributions to dentistry, in which, as in surgery, he showed himself as a preserver of ancient classical teaching. He used different instruments for loosening and removing teeth; he illustrated the first type of turn key for extraction, dental saws and files, dental scrapers, elevators and forceps for extraction of roots, methods of binding loose teeth to sound ones by gold and silver wire. He described also different kinds of oral deformities, dental arches and the insertion of artificial teeth, in all of which he was a pioneer.

Unfortunately, owing to religious prejudice, professional inertia and the baleful effect of such an enormous compilation, the surgery of Albucasis had no influence on his own people, and it was left to Western scholars to show sympathetic recognition to his endeavours. Though the bulk of the *al-Tasrif* was neglected, the section on surgery was translated by Gerard of Cremona and because of its excellent methods and lucid explanations it was eagerly adopted as the basic textbook from the middle of the thirteenth century onwards.

A fellow-countryman of Albucasis, Avenzoar of Seville (1072–1162), also practised surgery, though he admitted that few in his day were competent to do it. When speaking of the perforation of the cranium, he said: 'There are few these days who can carry out such an operation, and fewer still who have any understanding or experience of it. And so I advise the reader to find a teacher who has gained his expertise by practice, study, natural aptitude and long experience. No pupil should be allowed to practise surgery until he has served a long apprenticeship under an expert teacher

c

and operator.' When discussing other cases, he often remarked that, though he himself operated, he had never seen or heard of any one else who could do so. The reason was, that at that period Arab physicians considered it beneath their dignity to undertake any kind of manual operation, even if it involved the mere compounding of medicines:

> All other operations, such as phlebotomy, cautery, incision of arteries, etc., should be assigned to assistants. And to them should be left even more important operations such as incision of eyebrows, lifting veins which enlarge the whites of the eyes, and cataracts. The noble physician should do nothing but give advice about the medicine and diet of the patient, without undertaking any kind of manual operation, just as it is unseemly that he should make syrups and electuaries with his own hands. My own father never demeaned himself with any manual work of this kind during the whole course of his life.

The outstanding quality of Avenzoar was his clinical observation and his vivid description of diseases. He belonged to the Rhases tradition, placing the use of the senses on a higher level than theoretical reasoning. Among Arab authors he stood out as an exception by his surprising freedom in criticizing the sophistry, doctrinaire attitudes and obscurantism of his fellow physicians, who, he said, were more concerned about their 'sects' than about truth. Avenzoar's pages are enlivened with picturesque notes about his personal experiences in hospitals, prisons, towns, courts, even exile, and he recounts with disarming candour and simplicity both his successes and his failures, his sufferings and his fears. He often admits that he was less skilled in many things than his father, to whom, when in doubt, he had recourse for advice about treatment.

One interesting point that emerges from his book was the growing tendency of the time to distinguish between *medici* and *physici*, that is, between those who gave practical treatment for disease and those who merely studied it from the theoretical angle. When discussing the causes of hiccup, he gave certain reasons for his opinion, and then added: 'And these causes appear to me to be nearer the truth, since absolute truth is not necessary in the art of medicine. It is the job of natural science and theology to find absolute certainty and truth in this sphere, and so I will not assert that what I have said is true.' In another passage, he said: 'According to medical observation, such an organ would be called *neutrum* [i.e., getting better], because medical science only proceeds on evidence from the senses: but according to the reasoning of the *physici* [natural scientists] it would be called sick.'

Avenzoar, unlike Haly Abbas, would have no truck with astrology. He said that the spheres, stars, matter, form, time, place, and so on, were all created by God, and that without the will of God they could not possibly influence man either in his person or his actions. Consequently, he thought it nonsense to prescribe purging or bloodletting according to astrological indications. 'The wise scholars at Toledo contradict the assertions of astrologers, and say that the art of medicine is based on observation and diagnosis.' Likewise, he distrusted folk medicine and advised his readers against remedies recommended by *vulgares*.

Avenzoar was, then, an outstanding practitioner, whose ideas, had they been followed, would have ushered in a new era of medicine, freed from the bondage of authority and theory. Unfortunately, his advice and wise counsel fell on deaf ears.

A friend of Avenzoar was Averroes, born at Cordova in 1126 into a family of legists. His book, the *Colliget*, always follows Avenzoar's *al-Tesir* in the early printed editions. In extraordinary contrast to his friend's work, it is an extended commentary on Avicenna's *Canon*, less a medical than a philosophical treatise, addressed to those whose interest lies in natural philosophy and dialectics. Indeed, in the prologue he stated that one unversed in logic and the natural sciences would be unable to understand any part of his book, would derive no profit from it, and would abominate and despise it. It may be countered that even a scholar versed in both these sciences will find the book arid, prolix, devoid of practical content and wholly unacceptable as a book on medicine. Though he uses Galen frequently, he uses him as the basis for interminable argument and reaches banal conclusions, especially in therapeutics, which could have been reached much quicker by the use of common sense. In short, Averroes is Avicenna gone mad.

Unfortunately, this work had a wide circulation and exerted the most baneful influence on medieval medicine and philosophy.

Another native of Spain was Maimonides, born at Cordova in 1135. He was a Jew. Driven by religious persecution from Andalusia, he took refuge in Fez (1159) and, after a journey through Acre and Jerusalem, finally settled at Cairo, where his learning attracted recognition. He was appointed physician to the Vizier and to the sons of Saladin. His greatest achievements lay in the sphere of religion, in his commentaries on the Mischnah and in his *Guide to the Perplexed*. His writings on medicine, which include short treatises on asthma, hygiene, poisons and antidotes, haemorrhoids and a collection of aphorisms, though much prized in the West, added little to the store of knowledge handed down by previous writers, and his reputation has been much over-rated.

These are the writers from whom our knowledge of Arabic medicine is derived. They form only a fraction of the number whose works, in their hundreds, lie unpublished, even unexamined, in libraries all over the world. It is not possible, therefore, to pass a final judgement on the Arab achievement from the mere handful of texts which had the good fortune to be translated into Latin during the medieval period.

But certain characteristics emerge, which are probably typical of them all. Once the Arabs had amassed a large number of translations from the Greek, they no longer troubled to consult the original sources; furthermore they found the material too vast, too disparate, too uncongenial in spirit to assimilate thoroughly. Like the Byzantine writers whom they criticized, they soon began to make compilations, and as time progressed these compilations, and not the sources from which they were taken, became the sole objects of their study. This led to amalgams of ideas thrown together from totally different sources without any deep critical analysis. Their disposition to accept authority and uphold dogmatism (encouraged by the *Koran*) resulted in an unqualified acceptance of Galenism, whilst their inclination towards intellectual speculation resulted in dialectical acrobatics when they should have used their faculties for observation and clinical inspection. All this was reinforced by a penchant for systematisation which erected impressive structures, perfectly knit together to form an indestructible whole. Whilst early writers, like Rhases, whose knowledge was based on a first-hand acquaintance with Greek sources, were imbued with the spirit of Hippocrates, the later writers, bent on eclipsing the achievements of their forebears, luxuriated in meticulous pedantry and verbal quibbling. Hence, whilst the beginnings of Arab medicine provide superb examples of clinical observation and practical skill, the later days can show nothing but complicated uroscopy, highly sophisticated pulse-lore, and therapeutics calculated according to the principles of geometrical progression. Here and there, as in the case of Avenzoar, common sense and scepticism helped to keep at bay the tendency to make medicine subservient to philosophy, but on the whole philosophy and not medical science prevailed.

Chapter Three

Salerno

One of the earliest references to Salerno as a medical centre appears in the *Historia* of Richer, monk of Rheims, written towards the end of the tenth century. As a young man Richer had studied medicine under Gerbert at Rheims and had travelled to Chartres to read the *Aphorisms* of Hippocrates with Heribrand. His continued interest in medical matters is attested by the numerous passages in his book describing the symptoms and diseases of eminent people of his day. These descriptions of diseases were not based on first-hand information, but were copied almost verbatim from a text of Petrocellus and the Aurelius-Aesculapius complex which was available to him at Chartres. He was proud of this book knowledge and of the teachers who had instructed him, and in order to illustrate the superiority of the clerical medicine of France over the secular medicine of Italy he introduced into his text a story of a contest at the royal court between Derold, later Bishop of Amiens, and an unnamed Salernitan physician. Each physician tried to poison the other, but Derold's greater knowledge of drugs prevailed and the Salernitan paid for it with his life. Unhistorical though this tale may be, it points to two things: the reputation of Salerno as a centre for practical skill in medicine and the deficient book-knowledge of its representatives. Richer was aware that whilst Northern France had books, teachers, medical schools and practitioners, both clerical and lay, Salerno had at that time no celebrated doctors, no medical literature, no organized theoretical teaching and no established gild or corporation.

No medical text was associated with Salerno until the middle of the following century, when Gariopontus, a shadowy figure and perhaps a contemporary of St Peter Damian, produced his *Passionarius*, a compilation based on sources that went back to the fifth century. In spite of the appearance of Gariopontus' name on the title-page of an eleventh-century manuscript of the *Passionarius*, doubts have been expressed regarding both his authorship and his connection with Salerno. But even if these doubts are brushed aside, the contents of the book would do nothing to enhance the reputation of Salerno, but would merely show that by the middle of the eleventh century Salerno used the same medical sources as elsewhere and had made no progress beyond them.

The apogee of Salernitan medicine was not reached until the twelfth century, when the first medical texts, including the *Breslau codex*, made their appearance. This complex Salernitan literature included treatises on general therapy, fevers, urines, pulses and diets, as well as tracts on anatomy, the surgery of Roger and the *Antidotarium* of Nicholas, and it marked the emergence of Salerno as a teaching centre. This rise to eminence and importance was made possible by the labours of a monk at Monte Cassino named Constantine the African, a man of whom little is known beyond the fact that he was born in Carthage, travelled extensively in the East, and entered the abbey under Abbot Desiderius (later Pope Victor III), with whose encouragement he spent the rest of his life translating Arabic works of medicine into Latin. These translations enlarged considerably the range of medical knowledge at that time and, besides making available to the West a series of new texts, gave a powerful stimulus to explore still further the fields of ancient medical science. These translations, however, had been made in a monastery at some distance from Salerno and, as a result, their impact was not felt immediately.

The wide knowledge and the sound critical judgement of Constantine may be seen both in the list of authors and the varied topics which he selected for translation. Within a period of ten years he produced Latin versions of the *Al-Maliki* of Haly Abbas, the *Viaticus* and *Liber de stomacho* of Abu Djezzar, the *Liber de oculis* of Hunain, the *Liber diaetarum universalium et particu-*

larium of Isaac Judaeus together with his treatises *De urinis* and *De febribus*, the *Megatechne* of Galen (*De ingenio sanitatis*, abridged), the *De definitionibus* and *De elementis* of Isaac ibn Amaran, the *Liber graduum* of Mesue, and many others, some of which have not survived. These works cover the whole range of medicine, and represent some of the best writings produced by the Arabs. Later on and in another centre, Toledo, more medical texts were to be translated from the Arabic by Gerard of Cremona and his associates, but it was Constantine's pioneer effort which paved the way and gave to Salerno the opportunity of opening up new vistas in medicine.

How soon the influence of these translations began to make itself felt is impossible to decide, but the new version of Haly Abbas, made by Stephen of Antioch between May 1127 and January 1128, would seem to point to the early years of the twelfth century as the starting point. From that time forward there is increasing evidence that the new ideas were beginning to percolate through Salernitan teaching and most of the writers of this period quote Constantine's texts as their authorities, though they still lean heavily on the compilation of Gariopontus. The view that there was a rapid transformation of outlook cannot be sustained and the assertion that Salernitan writings display a realisation of the importance of theory in medicine, that they show keen observation, simple, unbiased interpretation and clear representation of morbid phenomena, that they replace methodism with Galenism, and so on, is an exaggeration. These are the characteristics which are said to distinguish the *Practica* of Bartholomew, the *Ars medendi* of the younger Copho, and the *Practica brevis* of Platearius. The *Practica* of Bartholomew (who was consulted both by Peter the Venerable and King Louis of France) scarcely merits the praise lavished on it, for it is no more than a meagre handbook for treating diseases. Based on Gariopontus, Constantine, John Afflacius, and the *Antidotarium* of Nicholas, with a few references to the aphorisms of Hippocrates, it gives the sketchiest description of diseases, sometimes no symptoms at all and immediately embarks on a list of remedies, few of which improve on those found in earlier texts. Theory is completely absent except at the beginning where medicine is defined, its parts described, properties of medicines given, and some rules laid down for diet and regimen. In some aspects the treatise is not as good as that of Gariopontus.

The *Ars medendi* of Copho, written down by one of his pupils from oral lectures, frequently quotes the aphorisms of Hippocrates and in some ways is little more than a commentary on them. It gives detailed instructions on the method of preparing medicines, mostly infusions of herbs in boiling water, and provides an alphabetical list of herbs or drugs which are effective in certain diseases. The three ways of treating the sick, which Copho describes, are a flat contradiction of the statement that methodism was ousted by Galenism at Salerno. The whole treatise is an elaboration of the methodist doctrine, stemming from Soranus and followed by all writers previous to Constantine, that patients are cured by dissolving the humours (purging), constricting them (with opiates) and restoring them (by food and drink). Copho, however, adds a fourth element, which he calls *digestion*, by which he means the elimination of purulent matter in internal abscesses. As for Platearius, his much vaunted personal observation may be judged by the fact that he considered putrefaction of the teeth to arise from the presence of worms: 'and this can be proved by sight, for when the teeth are washed with warm water, and water is poured into a vessel, the worms can be seen swimming about'. He thought toothache was caused by humours either descending from the brain or rising from the stomach, and the cure for it was bleeding in the first case, and vomiting in the second.

Perhaps the best synoptic view of early Salernitan medicine is to be found in the anonymous *De aegritudinum curatione*, which contains the teaching of John Afflacius, Matthew Platearius, Copho, Petronius, Bartholomaeus, Ferrarius and Trotula. This compendium, which probably served as a textbook for students, may be considered to reflect the scientific attainments of the most eminent masters there during the first half of the twelfth century. In general it cannot be said to show any distinct improvement on traditional 'monastic' medicine except in the greater use of diagnosis based on pulse and urine, and an emphasis on diet, both elements derived from the writings of Isaac Judaeus. A comparison of the chapters written by these men on diseases of the liver, spleen, lungs, and much else, with corresponding chapters in Petrocellus and Gariopontus, shows little if any progress: indeed, in many cases the descriptions of disease and symptoms are not as clear and detailed. Moreover, though diet plays a more important role, the therapeutics are neither more rational nor developed. Animal products like cats' dung, wolves' dung, mouse droppings, serpents' skin, lizards, urine of the patient mixed with food and so on abound; whilst superstitious customs, such as collecting herbs with prayers, wearing amulets, writing formulas on tree bark, all absent from Gariopontus, appear from time to time. Polypharmacy, so bitterly criticized in earlier writings, was also practised, sometimes as many as twenty-one ingredients being employed for one ointment or remedy.

The conclusion is that generalizations about the medical writings of Salerno are not valid, for they do not take into account the differences (and they are considerable) which separate the earlier from the later productions of this school.

About the middle of the twelfth century a change is discernible in the character of Salernitan writing, probably brought about by the production of works for teaching purposes. There was a steady progression from the purely practical manuals to theoretical treatises intended for the instruction of students, which, according to the prefaces, were composed at the express request of pupils and *socii*. The anatomical works are clearly addressed to an audience and oftentimes based on previous lectures given by masters: 'I follow here my teacher, Matthew Platearius, who, in his lectures on anatomy, pointed out everything for his pupils to see, and I describe nothing that I have not seen with my own eyes.' The first signs of this change are apparent in the commentaries, the first of which was made by Matthew Platearius on the *Antidotarium* of Nicholas, an antidotary transmitted by Greek and Latin writers with additions and modifications imported from Arabic sources. In a manuscript discovered by Kristeller, written about the middle of the century, this commentary is followed by five others on the following texts: the *Isagoge* of Johannitius, the *Tegni* of Galen, the *Aphorisms* and *Prognostics* of Hippocrates, and the *De urinis* of

Theophilus. The manuscript probably also contained a commentary on the *De pulsibus* of Philaretes. In short, it contained a complete set of commentaries on what was later to be known as the *Articella*, the basis of all medical teaching throughout the Middle Ages. The first two commentaries are attributed to Peter Musandinus 'taken down from the lectures of Bartholomew, an eminent theoretician in the art of medicine'. As Musandinus was the teacher of Gilles de Corbeil, who says that Maurus was younger, it points to a series of teachers: Bartholomew (whose *Practica* is mentioned above), Musandinus, his pupil, who wrote down what he heard from his master's lectures, and Maurus. From Maurus we have not only a commentary on the *Aphorisms* of Hippocrates, but an important manuscript, which contains his glosses on the group of medical texts already used by Musandinus. The significance of this development lies in the fact that the new texts recently translated from Greek and Arabic into Latin were selected as the basis for teaching, and the commentaries were the expression of the textual interpretation. This method of commentary was new to Salerno though it had been used earlier in the schools of liberal arts and had been transferred to the teaching of philosophy, theology and canon law. This method was to dominate the teaching of medicine for several centuries and gave rise to a copious literature, most of which has never been investigated.

Though the introduction of a literary approach to medicine gave it a more liberal flavour, there was another element which was to develop more strongly as time progressed. This was the philosophical approach. In the early commentaries there are quotations from Boethius, from the *Timaeus* of Plato and from the *Categories* of Aristotle, and references to other Aristotelian writings, such as the *Physics, Metaphysics,* the *De anima* and the *De generatione et corruptione.* How early this trend toward philosophical speculation in medicine had begun is uncertain, but the association of Guido of Arezzo, a professor of logic, with Roger Frugardi, the Salernitan surgeon, about 1170, may point to the introduction of the Aristotelian *Libri naturales* about that time. Certainly in the works of Urso of Calabria (d. 1225), in his *Aphorisms* and his two treatises *De effectibus qualitatum* and *De effectibus medicinae*, we see a well developed system of natural philosophy which was to form the basis of medical theory and practice.

The incorporation of this new element into medical teaching was not wholly beneficial: it did little to improve the understanding of disease, clinical observation or therapeutic treatment. Indeed, to some extent, it distracted attention from sense investigation and promoted dialectical arguments wherein the opinions of natural philosophers were pitted against the views of medical men. Henceforth the organs and functions of the body were to be discussed 'according to the physicians' and 'according to the philosophers' and endless arguments were to be tossed back and forth without advancing the knowledge of anatomy, symptomatology and diagnosis one step. If the medical writers of the school of Salerno can be credited with an important role in the diffusion of Aristotelian doctrines in the West, it can only be viewed, from the medical point of view, as the introduction of a wooden horse.

Though we see in the series of commentaries the emergence of a curriculum for the study of medicine at Salerno, with a group of standard texts as its basis, it cannot be assumed that the formation of the *Articella* is to be attributed to Bartholomew or to Salerno. Side by side with the commentaries by Salernitan masters, Kristeller discovered at least two others belonging to the twelfth century, different from those of Bartholomew and Musandinus, and showing no trace of Salernitan origin. Both of them appeared to have been composed, not in a school of medicine, but in a school of liberal arts, and one of them seemed to originate at Chartres. It is obvious that the curriculum was not yet stabilised and that the final selection of texts for study needed further consideration. Of the organisation of the school itself at Salerno we know nothing. The supposed existence of a College of Physicians, said to have been established as early as 1127, is based on a forged document of the fifteenth century and a misinterpretation of remarks made by Gilles de Corbeil. The sources of our knowledge of the institutional organisation of Salerno do not go beyond the thirteenth century, when the Emperor Frederick II published his regulations at Melfi in 1231. These regulations show nothing new and correspond to developments that had taken place at Paris and Bologna about 1220.

Salernitan medicine did not penetrate into England as quickly as some writers would like to believe. The *Peri Didaxeon*, which was supposed to have been the harbinger of a new trend in English medicine and to have stemmed from Salerno, is merely a part translation of the Petrocellus text available to the Anglo-Saxons in the ninth century. Moreover, it has no connection with Salerno. Nor can the complex of texts, written about the year 1085, and contained in MS 17 of St John's College, Oxford, be said to purvey any material that is recognizable as Salernitan. All the treatises contained in this manuscript reflect a type of medicine current in Europe before the rise of the South Italian school: the short treatise on phlebotomy can be paralleled in Bede, *De minutione sanguinis*, belonging to the eighth century; the passage on the four humours was known from the ninth century onwards; the regimen for the four temperaments, though having a counterpart in a text attributed to Giovanni Monaco, a pupil of Constantine, is also much older than the Salernitan school; whilst the prognostication of life and death derives from the various versions of the *Prognostica* attributed to Hippocrates or Democritus. The same remarks may be applied to the table of weights and measures, recipes for plasters and electuaries and other elements in the manuscript. The list of herbs, confidently asserted to be derived from the *Alphita* and 'wholly Salernitan' has, on the contrary, very little in common with it. In any case, the *Alphita* is probably French in origin.

That a change of outlook and a development of medical literature in England was effected during the eleventh century has been assumed because of the influx of scholars from Lorraine and Lotharingia. But it should be borne in mind that the interests of these men were mainly mathematical and astronomical, studies which do not necessarily imply an acquaintance with medicine. The promotion of most of them to high office, though having some influence on the intellectual standards in the church, did not automatically widen the horizon of medicine. Indeed, most of them attained eminence before the literary revival at Salerno took place. Duduc, Bishop of Wells in 1033, Leofric, Bishop of Crediton in 1046, Hermann, Bishop of Ramsbury in 1045, Giso, Bishop of Wells in 1060, the Athelard of Liège, appointed head of the college of canons at Earl Harold's foundation of Waltham, could not have had access to much medical literature which was not already available in England.

But at the Conquest in 1066 William brought in his train a group of distinguished physicians whose interests were predominantly medical, and it is to them that any change in outlook and any enrichment of medical literature must be attributed. Among this number (which included Aluricus, monk of St Bertin, John de Villula from Tours, later Bishop of Wells, Nigellus, and Goisbert), three stand out: Baldwin, monk of St Denys, later Abbot of Bury St Edmunds, Faricius of Arezzo, later Abbot of Abingdon, and Grimbald of Arezzo. All of them were described by their contemporaries as outstanding physicians, not merely because of their practical skill, but also because of their literary attainments. Of Faricius it is expressly said that he ordered a number of books 'de physica' to be written for the monastic library, and though the same might be presumed of Baldwin we have no definite evidence, since no manuscripts of his time have survived. We do know, however, that Lanfranc had medical books copied for Christ Church, Canterbury, and his successor, Anselm (like Lanfranc an Italian and a product of Bec), wrote to Albert for a copy of the *Aphorisms* of Hippocrates with glosses and a treatise on pulses. No trace of such texts is found in England before this time, so that some development in medical learning must have been taking place. None of this, however, can be called Salernitan medicine.

The first faint glimpses of influences from Salerno may be discerned in a few manuscripts which have survived from the early twelfth century: a Westminster copy of the *Liber melancholie* of Constantine, a Bury St Edmund's manuscript of Constantine's *Pantegni*, a *Passionarius Galieni* from Norwich Priory, the *Experimenta archiepiscopi Salernitani* (Alphanus, 1058–85) from Westminster, and an *Antidotarium Nicholai* from Durham. Other copies of Constantine were at Exeter, Battle and Canterbury. A more comprehensive collection of Salernitan texts, comprising the *Isagoge* of Johannitius, the *Aphorisms* of Hippocrates, a *Liber Galieni*, a *Liber urinarum Theophili*, a *Liber Philareti de negocio pulsuum* and a *Tegni Galieni*, which belonged to Lanercost Priory.

may have been made later in the century. Sometime between 1177 and 1194, Benedict, Abbot of Peterborough, gave to the abbey library a *Practica Bartholomaei*, and since the chronicler adds 'cum pluribus aliis rebus in uno volumine' it may indicate that the manuscript contained other Salernitan texts.

The earliest use of a Salernitan text in England seems to go back to the middle of the twelfth century. In his *Ars notaria*, written about 1174, John of Tilbury, a servant of Thomas, Archbishop of Canterbury, and probably a monk of St Albans, quoted a passage from the *Liber graduum* of Constantine, giving a recipe which he much recommended. As John was already an old man by 1174, it may be assumed that he had been acquainted with Constantine's text for some time, and this would fix the date at about the middle of the century. But a more significant quotation comes from Peter of Blois. Peter was one of many Englishmen who spent some time at the royal court in Sicily. The Chancellor of King Roger II had been an Englishman, Robert Selby, and his house was the meeting place for visitors like William of York and John of Salisbury. Peter of Blois was the tutor of William II and Gervase of Tilbury served under the same king. When Peter of Blois was travelling through France about 1175 he was called in consultation by another physician to give advice about the treatment of Gelduin of Amboise, who was suffering from fever. As Peter was in a hurry and could not await the arrival of his colleague, he wrote down a course of treatment to be followed. The text of this *Consilium* was published in the last century and has been acclaimed since as an enlightened and penetrating analysis of a man's symptoms. No one seems to have noticed that it is nothing less than a passage lifted bodily from Copho's treatise *De febribus*. Whatever one may think of Peter's honesty in passing this off as his own, the text proves that he was well acquainted with Salernitan medicine and possessed certain Salernitan medical texts. Though Peter is known to have studied at Bologna, there is no firm evidence that he had attended the schools at Salerno.

It is otherwise with four monks of St Albans, Warin (later abbot, 1185–95), his brother Matthew, and two others, Fabian and Robert de Salerno, who all entered the monastery on the same day and had all studied at Salerno. It may be surmised that when they joined the abbey they took their medical books with them, though none of them now survives. One of their confrères was Alexander Neckham, who was teaching in the abbey c. 1185. He had studied medicine along with theology, civil and canon law at Paris, but for medicine he gave pride of place to Salerno and Montpellier. The fact that Neckham does not enlarge on the studies either at Salerno or Montpellier, in marked contrast to his reminiscences of Paris and St Albans, would seem to indicate that he had not studied at either place. All the same there are traces in his writings of Salernitan influence and Brian Lawn has found no fewer than eighty out of 185 subjects which he had in common with the Salernitan *Questiones phisicales*. One of the masters to whom he owed most was Urso of Calabria. Neckham's own contribution to medicine, however, was minimal and his writings merely serve to show that for many learned men of his day the study of medicine was part of a general education, a theoretical rather than a practical undertaking. The list of books which he drew up outlining the curriculum to be followed in Paris throws light on the medical authors studied at that time and points to a strong similarity between the schools of Paris and Salerno. 'Anyone wishing to take up a course in medicine', he says, 'should attend lectures on Johannitius, on the *Aphorisms* and *Prognostica* of Hippocrates, and on the *Tegni* and *Pantegni* of Galen. The author of this work was Galen, the translator Constantine. He should attend lectures also on the *Diaetae*, universal and particular, of Isaac, on his book on urines, on the *Viaticum* of Constantine with the book on urines and pulses [by Theophilus], on Dioscorides and Macer, in which the nature of herbs is dealt with, and the books of Alexander [of Tralles].' If Neckham himself had followed this course at Paris (and there are indications that he did), there was little else for Salerno to offer.

Alexander had a friend, Alfred of Sareshal, who dedicated to him a work, *De motu cordis*. The interesting point is that, though Alfred deals with a medical subject, he shows only slight acquaintance with Constantine's translations and none at all with the Salernitan questions, in complete contrast to Alexander who makes extensive use of both. Moreover, he has a completely different approach. Whereas Alexander follows the more practical Salernitan attitude, Alfred lays greater emphasis on metaphysics and Aristotelian psychology and discusses everything from the point of view of the philosopher. This attitude had already been apparent among the Arabs much earlier and Avenzoar had criticized the division into *medici*, those who investigated things with their senses, and *physici*, those who based their conclusions on logical arguments. With Alfred of Sareshal this new approach is blatantly emphasised. He shows the greatest disdain for the *medici* whom he dubs 'mercenary healers of disease' and takes every opportunity of showing how worthless their opinions are. When speaking of the powers of the soul he says: 'Those of Montpellier and Salerno ascribe this to nature, but wrongly. And so it is easier to put medicine aside and to follow *physica* [*i.e.* theory].' He declares the doctors to be 'only *physici* in name' because the only books they have studied are Johannitius and the aphorisms of Hippocrates, whereas they have neglected the most important works of *physica*, meaning, obviously, the works of Aristotle. How far this pride in mere theory and logical argument could go is best shown by his discussion on the valves of the heart: 'There are those who say that the openings of the heart are not closed by muscles, but by certain films, disposed in a certain way and number. . . . *But whether this is so or not is not my concern.* . . . All the same some *physici* hold this opinion, and it is confirmed by the authority of the best anatomists.' Though he quotes Hippocrates, Galen and Isaac, it is evident that he merely wishes to extract from them what will support his philosophical theories, and his acceptance of their views depends entirely on whether they agree with his conclusions, arrived at on purely rational grounds. For instance, he notes that there is a disagreement about the number of chambers in the heart: 'The first and foremost anatomist, Abrugalis,' (*i.e.* Empedocles, as found in the Pseudo-Aristotle *De plantis*) 'who was a disciple of Galen, and the whole medical profession, say that the heart has only two chambers, but Aristotle states that there are three.' This he accepts; the 'mob of medical men', whom he puts on the same level as the 'illiterati', are condemned altogether.

The second part of Alfred's book deals with the formation of the foetus in the womb and, in particular, of the formation of the heart in the foetus. Here again arguments are based not so much on physical facts as on rational premises. It is in this section that he posits the influence of the planets on the formation of various parts of the body: the brain is formed under Mercury, the liver under Jupiter, and so on. The organs necessary for the operation of the vital spirits are formed first, then when the vital spirits are changed into animal spirits, the senses, like those of touch, begin to operate. The embryo does not begin to breathe until all the organs are perfectly formed.

Alfred's treatise is not an easy work to summarise, but it can be said that nothing of anatomical importance is discussed in it: everything stems from rational arguments based on the authority of Aristotle. But it is an important witness to the reception of the philosophical works of Aristotle and the influence they were beginning to have on the study of medicine.

The mention of monks in connection with the introduction of Salernitan doctrine into England reminds us that during the early medieval centuries the cloister was the most important repository for medical texts and the chief training ground of medical practitioners. Not only do our most precious texts of Hippocrates, Alexander of Tralles, Oribasius and Celsus come from monastic centres, but some also of the most celebrated physicians. Until the twelfth century this tradition had been tacitly accepted as normal, but during the course of that century certain abuses became manifest which called for measures that were completely to transform the practice of medicine in the cloister.

These abuses arose from the facility with which monks could leave their monasteries to attend the sick. Initially these absences from the monasteries had been made with the full knowledge and consent of the abbot, and in many cases they were encouraged because they brought prestige and even riches to the monastery. But often they brought dangers. Presence in the houses of the rich encouraged luxury in food and dress, led to idle habits and bred pride and arrogance, all inimical to monastic discipline and destructive of the religious spirit. When these abuses were brought to the attention of the Council convened at Rheims in 1131 under

Pope Innocent II, the response of the bishops was definite: in future all monks should abandon the practice of medicine for money. The abuse, however, was so widespread that mere local legislation was not sufficient. The prohibition was therefore renewed at the Council of the Lateran in 1139. On the pretext that medicine must be studied for the sake of treating members of the community, monks and canons continued to attend lectures on medicine in the schools, so a new decree was issued at the Council of Tours in 1163 forbidding all monks and canons to absent themselves from their abbeys for more than two months. Anyone who consented to their absence, whether bishop, abbot or prior, was to be excommunicated *ipso facto*. So firmly entrenched was the tradition that the prohibition had to be repeated several times: and no fewer than seven councils dealt with it between 1131 and 1212.

This prohibition did not apply to secular clerks, that is, to clerics not attached to an abbey or priory. Since the tenth century their part in medicine, both as regards study and practice, had been considerable, and most cathedral schools had produced both teachers and practitioners, some of whom had reached high office as a result of their knowledge and services. The position of these clerics was different from that of the monks and canons. At first they were attached to hospitals situated near the cathedrals, for they were bound to attend the church ceremonies besides looking after their patients. But when the monks were forbidden to study medicine or to leave their monasteries, the importance of the clerk physician increased and his responsibilities grew. In time, it was found necessary to relax the rules which bound him to a particular centre, so that whilst he attended the sick he could be absent from the town and from his choir duties. This was particularly so when he was attached to the royal service. But once more abuses crept in, and clerics were found neglecting their religious responsibilities to fulfil their role as physician.

Innocent III dealt with this matter at the Lateran Council of 1215. He forbade all clerics in higher orders, that is, subdeacons, deacons and priests, to carry out surgical operations which involved cutting or burning. It was to be left to laymen.

This decree has been constantly brought forward to show that from this point onwards surgery was thrown into the hands of the illiterate and that it led to the separation of medicine and surgery. This argument is based on three false suppositions: first, that until that moment the profession of surgery was flourishing; second, that it was wholly in the hands of clerics; third, that those who practised surgery henceforward were illiterate.

From the time of the disappearance of the school at Alexandria the practice of surgery had languished both in the East and the West. In the West no surgical texts of significance had survived: the works of Celsus, Oribasius and Paul of Aegina were not available except in one or two monastic centres (such as Fleury) where they were utterly neglected, and apart from fragments, such as the *Lecciones Eliodori,* the *Cyrurgia Eliodori,* lists of surgical instruments and one or two tracts on cautery, the technical writings necessary for surgical training were non-existent. In the East, where good surgical treatises were available and were copied into vast encyclopedias as part of the system of medicine, education, religion, traditional antipathy and inertia produced an equal stagnation. The Arabs, whilst possessing every opportunity to study, practise and further the science of surgery, disdained it, so that even with them surgery was left for the most part to quacks and charlatans. This we are told by Rhases, Haly Abbas, Albucasis and Avenzoar, four of the best Arab writers to deal with surgery.

Until the appearance of Constantine's translation of Haly Abbas' ninth book of the *Practica* the West had no systematic text of surgery to study. How then can one speak as if a professional body of highly trained surgeons existed at this time? Such surgeons as existed learned their profession by experience; they were practical, not necessarily educated or academically-trained men.

Secondly, although the Lateran decree makes it obvious that clerics had been acting as surgeons, it is equally obvious that laymen were not excluded since it expressly mentions them.

Thirdly, it is a gross error to imagine that education was limited to clerics. In the tenth, eleventh and twelfth centuries education was open to all. In the ninth century Alfred, in his prologue to Gregory's works, said that many could read English: in the tenth there were aldermen writing to Alcuin at Tours and even composing their own books, both in English and Latin. In the eleventh we hear of Lanfranc attracting to his school both laymen and nobles, whilst in the twelfth, Thibault of Étampes, who taught at Oxford, confessed that there were in England as many school-masters as tax-gatherers. London had at least three schools which laymen could attend, where the curriculum, judging by their dis-putations, covered not merely the liberal arts, but philosophy as well. It cannot be concluded that all who attended these schools were clerics or intending to be clerics. Godric of Finchale, a grown man, attended schools alongside small children. Parish priests taught in village schools, and were forbidden either to accept pay-ment for their services or to sell the school to other professional teachers. But there is one point further. The first surgical treatise produced in Medieval Europe was the so-called *Bamberg Surgery*, produced at Salerno about the beginning of the twelfth century. It consisted of 103 chapters, most of which had been copied verbatim from Constantine's translation of Haly Abbas, with additional material taken from the *Flebotomia Hippocrates* (known in the ninth century), from the *Euporistes* of Oribasius, from the *Epitome* of Vindician and from several older sources. Since Salernitan medi-cine at that period is acknowledged to have been for the most part in the hands of laymen, we may assume that the surgeons who used the text were laymen. This Bamberg text held the field until the middle of the twelfth century, when the work of Roger Frugardi, more methodical and detailed, but still based on essentially the same sources, became the popular text book of surgery. No evidence so far available mentions that Roger was other than a layman. The work, put into systematic order by his pupil, Guido of Arezzo (a grammarian and logician), in 1170 had immediate success and its influence spread beyond the narrow limits of Salerno: it was avidly studied both at Bologna and Montpellier, where it became the basis for numerous commentaries. Whether a surgeon who can read texts in Latin, compose his own book in Latin and presumably expound it to students in Latin is an *illiterate layman* is a rhetorical question. But this is the assumption on which medical writers, discussing the separation of medicine and surgery, have worked.

If there was a separation of surgery from medicine, it would appear to have taken its rise first among the Romans, for Galen admits that in his day there was a cleavage between physicians and surgeons. This tradition passed, through knowledge of Galen's works, to the Arabs. Already in the ninth century Rhases complained: 'Very rarely will you find a physician who has studied books on it [surgery] or learned it from a master who has studied it: indeed, those who operate are for the most part ignoramuses, rustics and boors. And for this reason evil diseases are bred in men.' Avenzoar, writing at the beginning of the twelfth century, said that not merely was surgery in the hands of the lower orders, but that no physician of his day would demean himself by carrying out any kind of manual operation, not merely of blood-letting, but even of compounding his own drugs.

The separation of surgery from medicine was not, therefore, an effect of ecclesiastical legislation: it was due not to the prohibition of medical practice to clerics, but to the influence of such texts as this which exalted the 'noble physician' to heights where any kind of manual operation was unthinkable. The physician's role, in Avenzoar's judgement, was to give consultations, advice, and instructions to his subordinates, but not to sully his hands. This is borne out by the attack of Jamerius Jamatus, a commentator on the *Surgery* of Roger, made at the beginning of the thirteenth century:

The unity [*integritati*] of medicine is greatly harmed by those who despise surgery and separate *physica* from it as if they were incompatible. For it is obvious to anyone who carefully examines the matter that the human body needs its help as much as other forms of medicine, since many illnesses admit no other cure. Many who try to disguise their laziness by heaping insults on a matter they know nothing about, assert that their hands should not be soiled by it [*non decere manus*]. But when these men call themselves eminent physicians and deem others unworthy of the name, should they not blush whenever surgery heals more quickly those whom they have left in desperate straits after trying every remedy? One could forgive their arrogance if they took the trouble to learn something about it, and did not hold up to ridicule both experts and learners. But they who despise small things fall little by little.

The famous phrase *Ecclesia abhorret a sanguine,* which has been quoted by every writer on medicine for the past two hundred years as the reason for the separation of surgery from medicine, is not to be found either in the text of the Council of Tours, 1163 A.D. (to which they all attribute it) or in any other Church Council. It cannot be found in the Decretals of the Popes nor in any of the medieval commentaries on canon law. It is a literary ghost. It owes its existence to Quesnay, the uncritical historian of the Faculty of Surgeons at Paris, who in 1774, citing a passage from Pasquier's *Recherches de la France* ('et comme l'église n'abhorre rien tant que le sang') translated it into Latin and put it into italics. No earlier source for this sentence can be found. Quesnay himself quoted a register from the archives of the Surgeons of Paris, in which it was stated that 'at the time of Boniface VIII (1294–1303) and Clement V (1305–14) a decree was put forth at Avignon and confirmed by the council of Philip le Bel that surgery was separated from medicine'. No such decree can be found in the register of Boniface VIII, whilst among the ten thousand documents contained in the register of Clement V only one refers to medicine, and that concerns itself with studies at Montpellier.

Chapter Four

Montpellier

In the meantime another school of medicine had risen to prominence, at Montpellier, in the South of France. By 1137 it appears to
have had a fully developed faculty of medicine, for in that year
Adalbert, later Archbishop of Mainz, studied there after complet-
ing his arts course in Paris, and somewhat later John of Salisbury,
speaking of those who left Paris to seek fame and fortune elsewhere, mentioned Montpellier as equal in its attractions to Salerno.
The earliest known official recognition of the medical faculty goes
back to the year 1180, when Guillem VIII decreed that no one
person should have the monopoly of teaching the natural sciences
(*physica*) there. 'I will not grant a concession or prerogative,' he
said, 'to any one person who shall have sole right to teach and hold
schools in the faculty of Physic at Montpellier . . . and therefore I
decree that anyone, from wheresoever he comes, may teach the
natural sciences at Montpellier.' This official statement was issued
probably with the idea of attracting more scholars and teachers
and of making Montpellier into a scholastic centre of equal importance with Paris and Salerno. Quite soon the faculty made its
presence felt by the refusal of the masters to accept without question the doctrines disseminated by the masters of Salerno, and
Gilles de Corbeil, writing at the end of the century, complained
bitterly that the school of Montpellier no longer trod in the same
paths as his beloved masters of Salerno, but had embraced the
'poisonous' doctrines of the Arabs. This is a strange remark to
make in view of the indebtedness of Salerno to Constantine's trans-

lations from Arabic writers. But he was obviously referring to the later translations from the Arabic which had been made at Toledo and which, through the proximity of Montpellier to Spain and the easier transmission of the new texts, had been quickly assimilated into the curriculum there. The work of the early translators, mainly concerned with astronomy and mathematics, had been carried on in many places, Barcelona, Tarazona, Segovia, Laon and Pamplona, as well as beyond the Pyrenees at Toulouse, Narbonne and Marseilles; and Montpellier was therefore favourably situated to take quick advantage of these new developments. Among the Englishmen who worked there and brought back the fruits of Arabic science may be named Adelard of Bath, Robert of Chester and Daniel Morley. But it was not until the middle of the century that fresh medical material was made available, when Gerard of Cremona and Mark of Toledo, besides translating a greater number of works belonging to Hippocrates and Galen, made excellent versions of Rhases' *Almansor,* Albucasis' *Chirurgia,* Avicenna's *Canon,* Isaac's *De elementis* and *De definitionibus,* Serapion's *Breviarium* and Al-Kindi's *De gradibus.* All these were works of the highest importance and it would seem from Gilles' disdainful remarks that under their influence Montpellier was outstripping the achievements of Salerno and attracting to itself more teachers and students. The school produced a number of celebrated masters during the course of the twelfth century. One of the earliest was probably Bernard le Provençal, who was a native of Arles, an alumnus of Salerno, and later master at Montpellier. In his commentary on the *Tabula Salerni* he makes several references to Montpellier and the teachers there. A treatise, *Signa mortis et vitae,* attributed to Ricardus Anglicus, may come from his pen. The Bodleian manuscript Rawlinson *c.* 543, which begins: *Tophimoto Polimitano ego peripateticus,* should also be attributed to him, since the opening words are undoubtedly a corruption of *Trophimopolitanus,* that is to say 'from the town of St Trophime', namely, Arles. Another teacher at the school was Matthew Salomon, who is supposed to have flourished about 1160. He was praised by Gilles de Corbeil for having saved the medical Faculty at Montpellier from complete eclipse:

Quo Pessulanus nisi Mons autore niteret
Jamdudum physice lux eclipsata fuisset.

Since Gilles calls him an author and not merely a lecturer or a teacher, he may be responsible for a treatise, *De pulsibus*, beginning *Corporis humani machina licet ex variis*, contained in a number of manuscripts. Among other notables from the same school Gilles mentions a certain Renaud, 'in medicinali doctor celeberrimus arte', who had lectured there for a considerable time and after becoming an eminent professor renounced his chair to enter the cloister, where he treated poor patients without fee.

At an early date English students found their way to Montpellier and some of our most eminent writers completed their training in this school.

An English writer whose works bear unmistakable marks of training both at Salerno and Montpellier is Ricardus Anglicus. Nothing is known of his career and for that reason he has long been confused with Richard of Wendover, canon of St Paul's and physician to Pope Gregory IX (1227–41), who died in 1252. Matthew of Paris, who knew Richard of Wendover well, nowhere attributes any medical writing to him, whereas Ricardus Anglicus was always associated with the *Micrologus*. The *Micrologus* is a collection of short treatises in which pathology, therapy (*causae, signa et curae*), practical pharmacy, prognostication and anatomy are respectively dealt with. The dedication of this work to Antelinus, Dean of Beauvais 1178–1190, effectively puts Richard in the twelfth century, though he may have survived into the thirteenth. That he was associated with Salerno seems proved by his frequent references to Salernitan writers, such as Archimateus, Platearius, Petrocellus and Ferrarius. He refers also to Archbishop Romuald who, himself a physician, had attended King William I of Sicily, who died of dysentery in 1166. He mentions the physician Gerard (not Gilbertus, as emended in Frer's edition of the *Practica*), who was called in to cure Queen Giovanna, wife of William II, of sterility: William II died in 1189. He also mentions Copho, Gerard (or Giraud of Bourges, the physician summoned to cure the Countess of Flanders), Constantine, Stephen (the translator of Haly

Abbas), and the *Antidotarium* of Nicholas. Besides this, he records that he had cured patients in Spoleto and Bologna, all details which would indicate that he had studied at Salerno. This is the reason no doubt why some manuscripts call him Ricardus Salernus.

But he had also been to Montpellier and probably taught there, for at the conclusion of his prologue to the work he remarks that 'Montpellier is my witness, that what I write is the fruit of study and experience'. His book, written with great freedom and clarity, enlivened by classical references and quotations from the poets, Horace and Juvenal, was evidently composed for the use of students who wilted at the thought of having to read the long and laborious works of the old authors. They wished to complete their studies as quickly and effortlessly as possible. Had this lazy attitude of modern students, he says, been encouraged in the old days, the spread of knowledge would have been impossible, 'for neither the logical arguments of Aristotle, nor the ethics of theologians, civil and canon lawyers, nor the *physica* of Apollo, Hippocrates and Galen, so propitious and helpful to nature, would have developed and held sway'. But nowadays students imagine they can travel from Gad to the Ganges in one day, even though they are on foot and are shackled with chains. No one in the medical profession can reach the top without effort and they who think they can, forget the aphorism of Hippocrates: lack of skill and ignorance deserve the fate of Phaeton, who fell from the skies in attempting a task beyond his strength. Yet out of compassion for such students he decided to give them some crumbs from his table, for in the end it was for the common good. The book was not to be published for fear of criticism from rivals, even though it was based on knowledge and experience. It was to be called *Micrologus*, because it was a brief manual of all medical knowledge available at that time, and should not be despised for its size, 'for even God is depicted in pictures as a little lamb'.

The *Practica* follows the usual head-to-foot procedure. It reveals nothing new on the whole, but has remarks which reveal both the independence and the common sense of the author. 'Let the reader note that I do not deal with certain affections, such as epilepsy, chronic toothache, paralysis, apoplexy, etc., because I think they are incurable and I could find nothing certain or the fruit of experience in the authors I have read, though there are some quacks who vainly try to cure them.' On another disease, gout, he says: 'The *Viaticum* is silent about this and has nothing useful to say, so I will not burden my pages with it, for I boldly assert that surgery and physic are useless, and so I consider it incurable and unworthy of attention.' Elsewhere, he remarks: 'I have spoken more fully on this subject because I have learned it by experience and through my cures I have gained the friendship of many nobles.'

Another part of the *Micrologus*, which bears the title *Signa*, has much in common with the *Practica*, but shows more traces of the early scholastic approach to medicine. It is based on Hippocrates, Galen, Rhases and Haly Abbas. In the very first paragraph he states that there are three periods in an illness to be considered, the onset, the increase, and the decline. His discussion of these terms, their divisions and subdivisions, reveal the dialectician, as do some of the words employed such as 'determine', 'distinguish'.

But Richard's most important contribution was his *Anatomia*, a treatise far more developed than Copho's and more detailed. In it he describes the division of members into the four principal organs, brain, liver, heart and testicles, and gives a full description of the brain, its faculties and the nerves which derive from it to inform the senses. There are several texts of this, some of which are really reworkings by a pupil named Nicholas, and Sudhoff thinks that only in those manuscripts where express reference is made to the *Micrologus* ('sicut in micrologo promissum est') can we be certain that the original text has been preserved. Its sources in general are not Salernitan, but the Constantinian translations; and Aristotle is named once. Some of the dialectical methods apparent in his treatise *De signis* occur also here and from time to time he brings forward the opinions of various authorities, compares them and then puts forward his own opinion. For instance: 'Galen says the brain has a cold quality, Aristotle says it has not.' 'According to Galen veins bring the blood from the liver to the testicles, but according to Hippocrates these veins come from the brain: personally I believe Galen.' 'On sperm and its production opinions vary.

Galen said that blood descends from all the organs and is changed from red into white sperm: Hippocrates said that the change is made in the brain and that the sperm descends to the testicles, for when they are cut no one can produce it: but there is no use in weighing these opinions.' One interesting passage recalls his own experience which he made to test the opinion both of Hippocrates and Bartholomaeus, the Salernitan physician. It concerned a certain noble matron who had unknowingly conceived. When a woman was pregnant, according to these two authorities, it was impossible to introduce even a needle into the womb for it closed so tightly that no opening was visible. As the woman complained of severe pains in the womb, Richard prescribed a pessary and, being a cleric and forbidden to carry out its positioning himself, he gave instructions to the midwife to do it. 'And both the patient and the midwife confessed to me that having tried every means, artifice and pressure they were unable, without incurring grave danger, to introduce the pessary into the orifice.' So Richard was able to 'prove their testimony by a manifest experiment' and so recalled the fact more easily to memory. This says much for his clinical observation and shows that in his case, at least, the purely intellectual and argumentative approach, contrasting one authority with another and deciding on a purely theoretical basis, did not eliminate altogether his practical training.

In one of the earliest texts of Ricardus Anglicus (Basle MS. D. III, 20) dating from the first decade of the thirteenth century, and bound together with works of Constantine, Gerard of Cremona, Bartholomaeus of Salerno, Maurus, Roger Frugardi and Gilles de Corbeil), there is a treatise *De naturalibus et medicinalibus* of Henry of Winchester. This shows that Henry belongs to the end of the twelfth or the early years of the thirteenth century. Two treatises belonging to him, *Medicinales questiones* and a *Flebotomia*, are found in two Oxford manuscripts of later date, but both titles and attribution are missing: only a fragment of the first (Corpus Christi MS. 490) bears a colophon *Explicit summa Magistri Henrici montis pessolani*. As there was a chancellor of Montpellier bearing the name Henricus de Guintonia in 1240, it may be that these two are one and the same person.

An examination of the *Medicinales questiones* reveals the sources on which the work was based: Plato's *Timaeus* in the translation and commentary of Chalcidius; Aristotle (*De generatione et corruptione*, and the pseudo-*Epistola ad Alexandrum*), Boethius' *De consolatione philosophiae*, Galen, Gariopontus, Oribasius on the *Aphorisms* of Hippocrates, Isaac Judaeus (*De urinis* and *De diaetis particularibus et universalibus*), Philaretes, Porphyry, Suetonius, Johannitius (*Isagoge*), Isaac's *De elementis*, Constantine's *Pantegni* and *Viaticum*, Seneca's *De naturalibus questionibus*, Remigius, Ovid, Jacobus Alkindi and Alexander. The classical quotations point to a rather early training in the schools, and his distinction drawn between dialectics and *phisica* infer a rather earlier phase of medical training than that given after the beginning of the thirteenth century. But the colophon describing him as of Montpellier is borne out by the rest of the texts from which he borrowed.

The purpose of the first book is described in the opening sentence of the prologue: 'The purpose of the present book is to go briefly over medical questions, so that disputants may have an easier entrance and the complex difficulty of the texts may be made clearer.' It was evidently the product of a teacher writing for his students. The writer immediately begins to discuss the definition of medicine given by Galen: 'Medicine is the science of the healthy, the sick and the convalescent', and the development of the work makes it obvious that it is a commentary on the *Isagoge* of Johannitius. He divides medicine into two parts, theoretical and practical, the latter being 'greatly inferior and more undignified'. The thirty-six chapters deal successively with matter, elements, humours, the members of the body, the faculties and powers, pulse, operations of the senses, vital spirit, age, sex and colour. All these fall under the heading of *res naturales*. From chapter sixteen onwards the treatise is concerned with *res non naturales*, namely food, air, drink, movement and rest, followed by ten chapters on *res contra naturam* which destroy or impair the health of the body. Here he discusses pain, various kinds of fevers, dropsy, and signs of sickness such as pulse and urine.

The treatise on phlebotomy in the same manuscript (Oxford

New College, MS. 171) begins: *Propositum est nobis tractare breviter in quibus egritudinibus competit flebotomia et de quibus venis.* The first sentence is identical with one that occurs in a widely used phlebotomy tract, and it is possible that this latter was based on Henry's work. A translation of this treatise is attributed specifically to Henry: 'And of fleubotomye these thyngs sufisyn aftir Maister Henricus Wyntonyensis' (Gonville and Caius MS. 176, fos. 1–11). Henry may have been responsible also for another tract on urinology, which begins: *Albus ut aqua, lacteus ut lac,* and which bears the colophon 'Et hec de urinis iuxta mag' H. It is curious that no mention is made elsewhere of this writer, except by Pelissier, writing in 1765. The general characteristics of his writings indicate that he flourished in the twelfth or early thirteenth century, when the study of *phisica* was gradually being differentiated from the liberal arts, and when medicine as a specialised profession had not yet taken complete hold. The medical authors he quotes are in general those of the *Articella,* and the technique he employs, though not so developed as that of Gilbertus Anglicus, shows some signs of the dialectical approach. His influence appears to have been minimal and judging by the contents of his books deserved little more. He is, however, a typical example of the university teacher of his time and provides evidence of English activity in the medical field.

Chapter Five

Medical Education

One feature common to all schools previous to the twelfth century, whether attached to a monastery or a cathedral, was their dependence on an individual. The early Anglo-Saxon schools, like those of the Irish, were grouped round famous scholars such as Theodore, Hadrian, Aldhelm of Malmesbury, Bede, Sedulius Scottus and John Eriugena. Whilst the reputation of the master could draw to him large groups of scholars and his school would flourish during his lifetime, the death of the master usually spelt the end of the school. Consequently there was lack of stability and continuity, little organisation and no recognised curriculum. So schools rose, prospered and disappeared, whether they were monastic, like Canterbury or Fleury, or secular, like Rheims and Chartres.

When the schools of Paris first came into prominence during the twelfth century it was on this tradition that they were based. William of Champeaux and his pupil Abelard attracted students from many places, and as the fame of Paris as a scholastic centre grew, so did the numbers of students and masters. To judge whether a pupil was fit to take on the responsibility of teaching others was left to the master, and hence some kind of test or examination must have been applied. But the passing of an examination or the conferring of a title could have had little value unless it was accepted and recognized by other authorities, either temporal or ecclesiastical; some kind of corporative corroboration was necessary. And thus the association of masters and students was at the basis of the movement which led eventually to the foundation of the university.

The curricula for the study of arts, theology and law appear to have been fixed at Paris about the third quarter of the twelfth century, to judge by the list of books recommended for these studies by Alexander of Neckham, and it is possible that the study of medicine followed the same trend. Whether this was imported from Salerno or Bologna is not clear, but it is quite certain that two masters of John Salisbury who had been to Bologna returned to Paris with new ideas about the organisation of studies. For at Bologna, where law was the main subject, a set curriculum with grades of study, and titles to distinguish the beginners from the more proficient, had been established at an early date.

Before this time, medical education at Paris had formed but one section of liberal studies and those who had wished to pursue their studies more methodically and professionally had betaken themselves to Salerno or Montpellier. Even at the end of the twelfth century Guy de Bazoches did not mention medicine as a separate branch of study when he said that arts, law and theology had their chosen abode on the Ile de la Cité. Further, in a letter (dated 1208–9) addressed by Innocent III to the masters of theology, law and the liberal arts, medicine was given no place, and even later, in 1231, Pope Gregory IX spoke of the 'masters of the *faculty* of arts and physic'.

It is not surprising, therefore, that the methods employed in the study of arts, theology and law, should be applied to the study of medicine. These had always been verbal commentary; each word was defined, its place set in the sentence, its meaning amplified, and the whole sense tested by argument. As in theology one sentence of scripture was illustrated by a similar sentence from another book of the Bible, and as in canon law one judgement in a decretal or conciliar decree was interpreted by reference to other papal utterances and conciliar decisions, so in medicine the terms, sentences and prescriptions were controlled by comparison with others. And just as the texts on which the theologians, canon lawyers and classical scholars commented were treated as sacrosanct, as monuments which were to be scrutinized for their meaning, but never changed, so were the medical texts treated. Instead, therefore, of medical students observing sick cases and finding out for themselves what diseases were, how they developed, how they reacted to forms of treatment and so on, they learned their medical texts like a catechism, always implicitly believing, hardly ever questioning, and rarely criticizing. Medical education was thus a matter of book-learning, a theoretical and speculative process, not necessarily associated with practise. This was a retrograde step, for even in the ninth century Walafrid Strabo, adding a comment to a medical text, had said: 'The science of medicine which is of the greatest use for men is divided into three parts, doctrine, reason and use. They are doctors by doctrine, who only learn or teach and do nothing practical. They are doctors by reason, who teach from experience. And they are doctors by use, who have not learned by books but by practical action.'

The curriculum followed by students at Paris began with twenty lectures on the *Isagoge* of Johannitius, a brief systematic survey of medicine, which dealt with elements, humours, powers, spirits, and the like (called the 'naturals'), changes in air and seasons, exercise, food, and baths (the 'non-naturals') and fevers, classes of sickness, their causes and treatment (called 'contra-naturals'). Fifty lectures were devoted to the *Aphorisms* of Hippocrates, twenty-six to the *Prognostics*, and thirty-eight to the *De regimine acutorum*. Then a lecture a week for about a year was given to the treatises on urines by Theophilus and Isaac Judaeus and those on pulses by Philaretus and Theophilus, and then Isaac's works on fevers and diets were studied. To these were added the *Viaticum* of Constantine. Later on, the curriculum was enlarged by the inclusion of works by Rhases, Avicenna and Galen.

We do not know in what order these books were studied, but since the course was spread over several years, there must have been some form of progression from the simpler to the more complicated and difficult texts. As part of the medical training disputations were held between October and Easter, and since subjects were chosen to which no definite answer could be given, they were called *Quodlibets*; that is, either a negative or positive attitude towards the problem could be defended. Naturally, all these questions were theoretical and the aptitude of the scholar was judged, not on his factual information, but on the dialectical skill with which he dealt with his opponents. According to statutes laid down in the thirteenth century, a scholar had to study medicine for four years before he could be admitted to the degree of bachelor (a term that appears for the first time in 1231). Later, the time was made more precise by demanding thirty-four months of active study from a student who already had a Master's degree in Arts, and thirty-six from others. In the fourteenth century these periods were lengthened; whilst, if a candidate came from another university, they would be doubled.

After completion of his term of study, the candidate submitted to two examinations, one in the presence of the regents of the Medical Faculty, the other before four masters. If all went well, he would be admitted Bachelor. This gave him an intermediate position between scholar and master, for he would give lectures to younger scholars whilst pursuing a higher course himself. His own course of lectures, four in number, consisted of three on theory and one on practice, all based on studies he had already completed. Two of the texts he lectured on were to have commentaries, and two not. This was described as *legendo cursorie*.

The next step in his education was the licentiate, conferred at Paris by the Chancellor of Notre Dame. If he were a Master of Arts, he had to prove by witnesses that he had studied medicine for five and a half years, otherwise for six years. In the fourteenth century these terms were lengthened, so that with the progress of time the tests became more searching. The licence was usually presented in the house of the Chancellor where masters of all three higher faculties, theology, law and arts, were present. Six months at least had to pass before the licentiate could receive the degree of Master, and then he had to submit to two examinations at which disputations took place. After his inception, the candidate was robed with the appropriate insignia, and then, after a further disputation, took his place among the Regent Masters. For a further two years he was bound to give lectures, *legere ordinarie*.

What of the practical side of the candidate's training? It was not until the middle of the fourteenth century, in Paris at least, that a decree was passed ordaining that no one should receive the degree of Master until he had practised for two summers outside Paris, or inside Paris under the supervision of another master, and it was not until another century had passed that this decree was extended to Bachelors of Medicine.

Though the foregoing remarks specifically refer to Paris, they were valid for Oxford, which modelled itself on the parent university. Exactly when medicine attained the dignity of a separate faculty there cannot be stated with certainty. In 1184–5 Giraldus Cambrensis referred to 'different faculties' at Oxford, though he did not specify them by name, but it would seem unlikely that medicine had achieved its independence by that date. That it did not achieve it in the subsequent fifty years is suggested by the fact that when Nicholas of Farnham returned to Oxford in 1229, after filling the post of professor of medicine at Bologna, he taught logic and natural philosophy. The establishment of an independent medical faculty at Oxford would not appear to have taken place earlier than the later decades of the thirteenth century, especially since at Paris, which gave the lead to Oxford, and later to Cambridge, the earliest statute of the medical faculty dates from 1273–4. The earliest mention of a medical faculty at Oxford occurs about 1303 when two statutes were carried by the Faculty of Arts and the Faculty of Medicine, there being but a single Regent Master of Medicine at the time.

Throughout the Middle Ages the Faculty of Medicine at Oxford appears to have been small and undistinguished. In 1414 there was only one doctor of medicine there available for teaching, and he was not an Englishman. A similar state of affairs existed at Cambridge, and in consequence neither of the English Universities produced a single physician of European reputation. Such Englishmen as did gain continental fame had studied abroad. In the fourteenth century tardy recognition of the Oxford medical faculty was given by Paris. In 1396, when Thomas Brown, a Master of Arts of Oxford, produced a notary's certificate that he had attended lectures on medicine there for six years and a half, the Paris faculty was willing, on condition that he obtained letters patent under the seal of the medical faculty of Oxford, to allow his time spent in study to count as three years in Paris.

In some Oxford Colleges the study of medicine was discouraged. At Merton it was expressly forbidden by statute. In 1284 at Archbishop Peckham's visitation, one of the 'abuses' to be corrected was the study of medicine, on the plea that it was a branch of *'phisica'*. When New College was founded in 1379 the statutes provided that whereas out of a total of seventy fellows ten were to study law and ten civil law, only two might study medicine. The rest were to concentrate on theology and the arts. Those who studied medicine were required to take priestly orders later, and since it was forbidden for priests to lecture in medicine, it can be seen that there was lack of continuity in teaching and a loss of personnel in the medical faculty. At Magdalen only one fellow out of a total of forty was allowed to study medicine after receiving special leave. It is not surprising that the number of masters of medicine from Oxford was small.

It is not possible to say at what date a separate faculty of medicine emerged at Cambridge. The university archives were destroyed by fire in the riots of 1381 and the surviving printed statutes, earlier than the fifteenth century, are fragmentary; the thirteenth-century text has not yet been published. That such a faculty was in existence about the middle of the fourteenth century may be inferred from the code of statutes framed for Peterhouse, which provided that out of fourteen students, one should be allowed to study medicine. The foundation of Pembroke College three years later for thirty scholars also provided for one of its fellows to pursue the study of medicine, whilst at Gonville, 1351, two fellows could choose to enter the faculty of medicine. At Cambridge the medical faculty was even more inconspicuous than at Oxford. In the fifteenth century statutes had to make provision for the proctors to present candidates for medical degrees in cases where no doctor of medicine was available. This indicates how poorly served they were. The number of degrees taken in the various faculties between 1488 and 1511 underlines the relative backwardness of the medical faculty: out of 3827 candidates only twenty-eight took degrees in medicine, and this was over a period of thirty-three years. The arts students were more than a hundred times larger in numbers. Further evidence of the neglect of medicine at the English universities at the close of the Middle Ages is reflected in the lists of Cautions recorded in the Cambridge Grace Books A and B between 1454 and 1544. These pledges frequently consisted of books, although after 1500, when printing began to reduce the intrinsic value of manuscripts, deposits were made of plate, astrolabes and other scientific instruments. Out of 746 books deposited as pledges during this period only seven were medical books.

Although at Oxford there is no evidence of a statute governing the degree of Bachelor of Medicine, a form was prescribed for those incepting in medicine some time before 1350. There it was laid down that they must first have read in Arts before they were licensed to incept. They must have attended lectures on medicine for six years, have given a course of lectures on one practical treatise (the *Regimen acutorum* of Hippocrates, or the *Liber febrium* of Isaac), and on one theoretical text (the *Liber Tegni* of Galen, or the *Aphorisms* of Hippocrates). They must have defended certain theses publicly and also acted as opponents to others who defended theses. For those who did not possess an M.A. degree, the conditions were that they must have been previously admitted to practice and have given lectures for two years. So, in medieval days, to reach a mastership or doctorate in medicine required a minimum of thirteen or fifteen years at the university, after which the doctor was required to remain in residence and lecture for a further two years. In the same statute provision was made for Masters of Arts to be present at the candidate's disputations on account of the insufficient number of regents in the Faculty of Medicine. As they were to assist in judging of the candidate's fitness, it is quite clear that medical ability was judged mainly on the candidate's cleverness in arguing and reasoning logically, and not in his observation or practical application of his book knowledge.

There were some exceptions to the normal progress from degrees in arts to the doctorate in medicine, most of which appear to have arisen from interruptions in study due to going into practice. On the other hand, since dispensations were a continual source of revenue to the university authorities, financial considerations may have influenced these decisions. In 1459, for example, William

Hobbys supplicated that three years' study in the Faculty of Medicine and twelve spent in practice outside the University, might suffice to allow him to lecture on the *Aphorisms* of Hippocrates, in other words, might give him the M.B. In 1455 John Bylsdon, 'bachelor in the faculty of medicine', supplicated that fifteen years of theory and practise in the faculty, together with four public responsions, attending lectures for the same number of years and lecturing on the *Aphorisms* and *Prognostics* might suffice to allow him to incept in medicine. The first request was granted on payment of twenty shillings, the second on condition that he repair the windows in the hall of Congregation.

The earliest evidence of the procedure for giving the *licentia practicandi* at Oxford derives from a statute dating from before 1350. It prescribes the 'Form according to which practitioners in medicine are to be admitted'. This seems to be a repetition of an earlier statute to which reference is made. It provides 'that because those who are famed for their practice in Oxford and those who have attained the mastership in medicine are considered to be so much more able than others; and cures of disease, mortal illnesses and the regimen of health are more confidently entrusted to their care, it is obviously dangerous to permit anyone either to incept or to practise in Oxford, unless he is judged to be suitable. . . .' It was therefore decreed that 'no physician undertake the cure of the sick in the municipality of Oxford by giving medical treatment unless he had attended lectures on medicine for four years and been examined by the regent masters of the faculty on his practical knowledge'. Those who had not been regents in the faculty were not allowed to incept nor practise until it could be proved that they had attended lectures for eight years, had been examined and had been admitted by the Chancellor to practise. This procedure was closely related to that of Paris where originally the candidate was examined by the Chancellor.

Chapter Six

Gilbertus Anglicus and Others

The type of education given at the universities in the twelfth and thirteenth centuries is well illustrated by the work of one of the earliest English writers on medicine, Gilbertus Anglicus. There has been great controversy regarding the exact date when he lived, practised and wrote his *Compendium medicinae*, but evidence would seem to point to the first quarter of the thirteenth century as his most active period. The oldest manuscript of his work is dated 1271 (Bruges MS. 469) where he is called De Aquila, which was an honour in the county of Essex. Many Gilberts are named in the De Aquila family, which flourished for almost two centuries before losing its lands, but whether the physician was a member of it is doubtful. There was a physician of this name who attended Archbishop Hubert Walter (d. 1204), whilst the writer of the *Compendium* says he had attended a Count of Forez (who may be Guiges III, who died in the Holy Land in 1202) and Bertrand, son of Lord Hugues of Djebail in Syria. A Gilbertus Anglicus, physician, was also active about 1230. It would seem probable that they are all one and the same man.

Though he wrote several other works, such as a commentary on the *De urinis* of Gilles de Corbeil (d. 1212), a commentary on the *Aphorisms* of Hippocrates (Bod. MS. 720) and probably an *Antidotarium* (Gonville and Caius MS. 379), it was the *Compendium* which later acquired such renown that Chaucer named Gilbert among the famous authors studied by his 'doctor of Physik'. This work makes no claim to originality, as its opening words confess: 'Here begins the book of diseases, particular and universal, written by master Gilbert, extracted and excerpted from all the authors and from the practical manuals of the Masters.' The authorities quoted by him cover a wide field: Pythagoras, Hippocrates, Aristotle, Galen (really Gariopontus), Rufus of Ephesus, Alexander of Tralles, Theodorus Priscianus, Theophilus, Philaretes, Stephen of Antioch, Rhases, Haly Abbas, Isaac Judaeus, Joannitius, Avicenna, besides several Salernitan writers such as Constantinus Africanus, Nicholas, Platearius, Ferrarius, Ricardus Anglicus, and Maurus. Some of these writers were those specified in the curriculum of the University of Paris, but there are others, notably the Salernitans and the Arabs, who had not been accepted there until a later period. We may surmise then, that though he may have studied at Paris, it is much more likely that he was a product of Salerno and Montpellier, where Arabic medicine had been received with enthusiasm. Though his reading is voluminous, his reliance on his authorities is great. From time to time he interjects his own opinions, but this is done with diffidence. Usually he is content to list conflicting opinions, theories or treatments, and to choose one of them at the end. This was the scholastic method of the twelfth century, first introduced by the *Sic et Non* of Abelard, where views of equally great authorities were pitted one against the other and an opinion expressed on their reasonableness.

It is quite obvious that Gilbert had studied scholastic philosophy, for into his work he introduces the method of syllogistic reasoning, with its peculiar terminology employed in debates, to bear upon purely medical problems. He speaks of efficient, formal, material and final causes, substance and accident, genus and species, differences of essence and being, and so on. Moreover, the chapters themselves are modelled on the same plan as the *Summa* of Thomas Aquinas with their examination of various authorities, which are discarded or accepted, and settled by a final judgement. A short extract from one of the early chapters on fever will demonstrate this method:

Johannitius says that fever is unnatural heat going beyond nature, proceeding from the heart and injuring the arteries by its effect. On

73

this definition there is some doubt among authors, whether it is made according to essence, or cause, or some other way. Constantine says this definition is taken from the essence of fever, that is, from the heat going beyond nature, and not from the accidents that accompany fever, and this is held by other medical writers. But the contrary seems true, for if fever is essential heat, then in the same way health is heat: and so health and disease are the same ... And if it is said that health and disease are different kinds of heat, since disease is unnatural heat and health is natural heat, yet they do not appear to differ, since natural and unnatural heat, insofar as they are formal properties of an organ, do not differ substantially and only accidentally, like black and white dice.

Constantine says that fever is extraneous heat, separable from the organs. But natural heat is not separable from the organs while life is present. Therefore the heat of fever is not natural.

Here we see syllogistic reasoning, based on Aristotelian logic, being used to sift the truth of arguments put forward by various medical writers. No facts are adduced, no clinical observation is put forward to decide the question. It is all a matter of reasoning and argument. This was typical of the university education for the medical student of the time, and the 'disputations', 'responsions', 'oppositions', 'defending theses' and so on refer to this method employed by Gilbert in his *Compendium*.

The manner of comment on a text is also reminiscent of the manner in which teaching was carried out. For instance:

Aristotle says that in the soul there are no images but only images of images. Hence he adds: 'taken from the likenesses of coloured bodies which are the proper object of sense.' When he says *formed*, he draws attention to its proper objects; hence, not colour, but coloured things are apprehended, since sight is a corporeal sense. When he says *coming*, he means that a distance is required between the seer and the things seen. And when he says *bodies*, he shows that there are divers media, and he puts it in the plural because there are many things between the seer and the thing seen, like air and water.

The whole of this particular chapter on the eye shows at once the strength and the weakness of this method. First there is the exegesis of the text, carried out exactly as if it were a literary or scriptural passage, with explanations of each single word. Next comes the argument supported by syllogisms, with its premises and conclusions. Finally there are the opinions of other authors quoted either to contradict or support the conclusion.

Though Gilbert's work shows this weakness, there are also compensating virtues. One of these is the logical way in which the *Compendium* is built up. Though he follows (after a long section on fevers) the age-long tradition of treating diseases according to the limbs of the body, beginning with the head and proceeding to the feet, within these limits everything is orderly and methodical. Matters are treated in great detail and practically no aspect of a disease is left undescribed. Moreover he gives long lists of remedies and modes of treatment for each ailment or disease, though he is not always satisfied that every eventuality has been covered. When treating of the affections of the ear, for instance, he says: 'But the physician should supply by his own industry what authors have omitted to say, for authors only give examples and for the sake of brevity leave many things unsaid. A physician will be judged worthy of admiration and fame according as he discovers for himself by hard study and actual practice what is best.' This indicates that he considered experiment and invention to be a necessary part of the equipment of a good physician. He shows this in his own case by differing several times from accepted forms of treatment and quoting his own personal experience. A little caution, however, should be exercised in accepting all Gilbert's statements which pretend to describe his personal actions. An appendix (No. 5) printed by Withington which purports to give the text of Gilbert's treatment in a case of gout turns out, on examination, to be nothing more than the transcription, word for word, of a passage from Rhases, *De egritudinibus juncturarum*. The same may be said for many other parts of the *Compendium*. Let us take Gilbert's discussion of leprosy, which is generally acknowledged to be one of his outstanding achievements and which, according to some writers, is the first correct description of this disease in the West. The symptoms listed by Gilbert mention permanent loss of sensation affecting particularly the fingers and toes; coldness and formication in the affected parts; transparency of the skin with the loss of its natural folds; distortion of the joints of the hands and feet, the mouth or nose; a tickling sensation within the body, arms and lips as if some live creature were fluttering within; fetor of breath, of perspiration and of the skin, and a loss of hair on the limbs which are covered with other fine hairs almost invisible unless held up to the sun. Much of this can be found already in Ricardus Anglicus and much also in the even earlier author, Haly Abbas.

Some other parts of Gilbert's work, which appear to be the result of personal observation, also come under this category. Gilbert, like all medieval writers, considered that mania and melancholia were due to disturbances of the anterior or middle cell of the brain by which imagination or reason were diminished. To demonstrate this he gave two examples. The first was of a man suffering from melancholy, who was asked by his master to take care of some glass vases. When the melancholic patient recognized a friend passing in the street, he asked him: 'Do you want some glass vases?' and when the friend answered 'Yes', he threw them down at his feet and smashed them. This, says Gilbert, is proof that his imagination was not at fault, because he recognized his friend. But his reason was disturbed, because he did not realise that glass vases were fragile. In the case of mania, he told the story of a young man, who ran from the house followed by his father, who tried to bring him back. The maniac struck his father violently, and when the father remonstrated and asked: 'Why did you strike your father?', the maniac fell at his feet and begged his pardon. Here, says Gilbert, the imagination was disturbed, because he did not recognize his father: but his reason was intact, because he knew that it was wrong to strike a parent.

Gilbert goes on to distinguish various kinds of mental disturbance with their expressions and symptoms:

Some weep, others dance, others give expression to the most fantastic opinions and think they are true, so they fear to be touched lest they burst, or they think they have no head, or that they carry frogs in their bellies, or they think they have seen devils and in their fury strike others. But the common symptoms which are universal are: they suffer sadness, and irrational fears, they have a sense of impending doom and feel what does not exist. For they see things before their eyes, terrible, black shapes like monks, demons and black men threatening to kill them. Some think they are ascending to the sky, others are terrified of falling. Yet all have one thing in common: they have an insatiable desire for medicine. They implore the doctors to give them remedies for which they will part with their most precious possessions: but when it comes to the point, they will neither listen to the doctor nor carry out his orders.

Gilbert has a great deal more in this vein. But it all comes ultimately from Galen through the medium of Constantine.

In dealing with such patients Gilbert says that since, in melancholia, they suffer most from fear, they should above all be given a sense of security: their disturbed imagination should be corrected with rational arguments and their suspicions allayed by ingenious stratagems. Music, sweet smelling herbs and wine should be given to them. As regards the body, since they suffer from thinness, lack of sleep, brooding, loss of appetite, worry and too much anxious thought, physical remedies, and particularly diet, should be applied.

As will be seen, Gilbert's notions are quite reasonable: in fact, they are in advance of some methods employed in later centuries for the correction of mentally disturbed people. But these ideas cannot be said to be personal. On the other hand it should be recognized that he does not have recourse to demons and diabolical possession in order to explain the condition of maniacs and melancholics, a view which is commonly held of medieval attitudes to these mental states.

Another part of Gilbert's book which has been singled out for commendation is the closing section on hygiene for travellers by land and sea. Before making a journey over land, Gilbert counsels a preliminary purgation, a good bath, ample meals to build up one's strength, electuaries to guard against the heat in summer, and heating electuaries to guard against the damp and misty air in winter. Some, he says, take with them a little earth from their own country and mix it with the water of the places they visit as a precautionary measure. On the journey itself the traveller should avoid over-eating or drinking, but if he has a heavy meal he should sleep before continuing on the road, whatever the hour may be. Every evening he should take a light supper, wash his feet in hot water and rub his soles with salt. On hot days he should keep his head covered, and quench his thirst with vinegar and water. Bread at least three days old should be preferred for meals, together with goat-flesh, pork, poultry, fish that have scales, but no milk products should be taken except in the evening. On travel by sea, Gilbert emphasises the chief points to be considered: the prevention of nausea and vomiting, the avoidance of foul smells on the ship and the quenching of thirst. To prevent nausea he recommends the juice of pomegranates, lemons or a decoction of parsley. The traveller should sit with his head erect and instead of looking around him, should keep his eyes fixed on one object. He should also support himself by grasping firmly the beams of the ship. To prevent belching he should suck something sweet or chew seeds. If he becomes sea-sick, he should suck sour pomegranates and eat nothing until his stomach is settled. Then he may take a comforting drink of dyantos. Since most of the food on board ship is salty, it should be cooked in three or four different sets of water.

To overcome the stench of the ship, he should have sweet-smelling electuaries, and after each meal should chew cloves or musk, or amber, and carry an amber apple in his hand and put it to his nose. As far as possible he should keep clear of the bilge channels by walking on the top deck. And to avoid fleas and lice his clothes should be washed frequently.

To quench his thirst he should eat citrous fruits. But drinking water ought to be purified by allowing it to trickle through fresh air, by boiling, straining and allowing the sediment to settle. The rich may distil water in an alembic, but it can also be done by putting a little lemon or vinegar into it.

All this is sensible advice. But it is not Gilbert's. He got it from Rhases, who copied it from Paul of Aegina, who extracted it from Oribasius, who compiled it from Diocles. But Gilbert was not the only writer to pass this off as his own; so did Avicenna, Arnold of Villanova, Bernard Gordon, John Gaddesden and various others.

One topic on which Gilbert may be the first physician to have given some new ideas was that of small-pox. It is generally said that John Gaddesden was the first to have cured it by enclosing the patient in thick red curtains; but Gilbert gives an earlier version of this treatment: 'Old women in Provence give burnt purple cloth mixed with liquid as a drink, for its hidden properties are said to cure small-pox.' He is also said to provide the earliest discussion by an English physician on the gout, for, as we have seen, Ricardus Anglicus considered it to be incurable. He prescribed colchicum. But whether one should say that this remedy was known only to peripatetic herbalists and 'empirics' and class Gilbert among them is doubtful. Colchicum or hermodactyl had been used for centuries before this time and was to be used by reputable physicians for a long time to come, certainly after 1282, when, according to some writers, it was used for the last time.

An interesting facet of Gilbert's work is his preoccupation with surgery. In view of the opinion that after 1215 surgery and medicine were separated and that a certain antagonism existed between physicians and surgeons, his attitude is of some importance. Gilbert's surgical chapters present as complete and scientific a view of surgery as any contemporaneous writings even from Italy, and this should not be surprising since most of them are taken bodily from Roger's *Chirurgia*. But as he was a physician, one would hardly expect it. He discusses wounds of the head, neck, throat, nerves, oesophagus, scapula, clavicle; fractures of the arm, forearm and ribs; dislocation of the jaw, shoulder and elbows; fistulae in various parts of the body; operations on tonsils, uvula, hernia, stone and other things. All these matters are discussed at great length and with a surprising amount of detail regarding symptoms and treatment. He does not merely record these details, but expresses his opinion as a physician about them. He even counsels the physician not to meddle with them in certain cases because they are too dangerous. One case may even describe his own experience. When dealing with stone he says:

I once met a man suffering from this condition, who complained of severe pain in the urinary passage as I was introducing the sound. I recognized that there were wounds in the same part, because as soon as these were touched by the sound, the urine began to flow, followed soon after by a trickle of blood and fleshy particles. . . . *We get no help from modern physicians where the treatment of this is concerned, for what they busy themselves with is dialectics rather than rational medicine.* The main job of a physician is to know for certain that obstruction to the passage of urine is due to no other cause than stone or the presence of blood clots.

In this chapter no mention is made of lithotomy, but later on he discusses the whole matter at length and gives a description of the way in which the operation should be carried out. All these details would hardly have been incorporated into the *Compendium* – a work addressed to physicians – if they were not intended to be followed and employed. And the conclusion must be that the so-called division between surgeons and physicians was not, at the time he wrote the book, so pronounced as had been supposed. What is certain is that Gilbert himself had no disdain for surgery. The same attitude can be found on every page of the *Practica* of Ricardus Anglicus.

The final portion of Gilbert's work deals with gynaecology. It has its illustrious forbear in the *De passionibus mulierum* of Trotula, the Salernitan midwife, but it surpasses this, both in detail and in general treatment. He has nothing but contempt for certain Masters who advise what Gilbert considers to be both against nature and against the Christian law *cum suis cartabellis nepharia scrutantes*; they should be ground to dust and scattered to the winds, he says. What is surprising is the fact that though Gilbert has passages which appear to derive from Soranus, he does not mention him. Soranus, who had merited the epithet 'the accoucheur' for his skill in dealing with women's ailments and his rational teaching, had been used by Oribasius, Aetius of Amida, Paul of Aegina, and through them had passed to the Arabs. Theodorus Priscianus had based his third book of the *Euporista* on Soranus' teaching and later Aurelianus had made a paraphrase of it, concentrating his attention on the diagnostic and therapeutic sections. About 500 A.D. Muscio used it extensively, particularly the shorter catechism written by Soranus for midwives, and his text, originally written in Latin, but later translated into Greek, gave rise to the misconception that the compiler was a Greek called Moschion. This latter text was adorned with many illustrations showing the various presentations of the foetus with short instructions on how to deal with them. The earliest extant manuscripts of this treatise go back to the ninth century, but there was one in England in the twelfth century, as can be seen by the few illustrations, accompanied with a partial text, surviving in MS. Ashmole 399. In view of Gilbert's treatment of gynaecological matters, it may be useful to correct some misunderstandings which have arisen regarding this Ashmole manuscript, and the illustrations it contains, particularly since they have attained some notoriety.

The manuscript was first prepared about the middle of the twelfth century, as is proved by the treatise on physiognomy, printed by Rose, and dated 1152. At the same time various pages were filled with illustrations, some pertaining to the treatise of Muscio, five comprising the Alexandrian series of bones, nerves, veins, and so on, and others depicting different organs of the body, such as the liver, kidneys, spleen, womb. No texts accompanied these last two series and the manuscript was left incomplete. Later in the thirteenth century someone filled up the pages with treatises, carefully writing round the illustrations, but adding texts which had nothing in common with the pictures, for instance, the *De coitu* of Constantine, the *De spermate*, and Constantine's treatise *De stomacho* addressed to Archbishop Alphanus of Salerno: the pages depicting various organs of the body has been filled with Trotula, *De passionibus mulierum.*

On folios 33–34v there is a series of six illustrations in which women's ailments are the main theme, and which has formed the basis of many articles, none of which supply the true interpretation. The drawings (with the exception of the last two, which all writers acknowledge have no connection with the main series) are literal illustrations of the text by Trotula and the *Anatomia Ricardi.* They are not pictures of a case history but of the various ailments which afflict women. The first picture illustrates retention of menstrua with symptoms described by Trotula: 'Prolonged retention of menstrua affects women so gravely that they appear to be dead. For the vapour, long closed in, rises to the spiritual members, affects the brain, oppresses the noble members and all those in the breast . . . and they lose consciousness and cannot speak. Their pulse is slow and weak and sometimes so faint that they seem to be dead.' The second picture illustrates suffocation of the matrix: 'Her knees are drawn up towards her head, she cannot see, . . .' And the cure is twofold: 'Put fetid smelling things to her nose . . . or place them on burning coals so that the smoke rising to her nostrils can cure her.' The third picture illustrates the method of discovering whether the patient, suffering from either of these two ailments, is dead or not: 'Place a little vessel full of water on her breast; if it moves, she is alive, but if not, she is dead.' The fourth illustration refers to the types of women who suffer most from suffocation of the matrix, namely virgins and widows, whose natural instincts have had no outlet. The fifth refers to a urine analysis of a woman in pregnancy. The last picture of a dissection, though it has a woman for its subject, is not necessarily bound up with the gynaecological series, but with the *Anatomia Ricardi* in the same MS: it represents a dissector acting under the instructions of a physician, with all the organs being shown which had been illustrated in exactly the same way on an earlier page of the manuscript. Had previous writers examined these earlier drawings they would not have come to the conclusion that the object in the dissector's hand was a mandrake, inserted to procure abortion; they would have seen that it was the liver. It is not necessary to investigate all the details which occur in the drawings, for they are easily explainable in the light of the Trotula treatise.

Gilbert has dealt at length with these matters in the final section of his *Compendium*: he describes the same symptoms, prescribes the same remedies, and shows himself to be perfectly experienced in this branch of medicine. As we have said, he shows no awareness of the works of Muscio and does not appear to have read Aurelius' paraphrase of Soranus, a copy of which apparently belonged to St Augustine's, Canterbury, in the thirteenth century.

After Gilbertus Anglicus no important author appeared on the English scene during the thirteenth century. A certain John of St Giles who, according to Trivet, was a most skilful physician and had lectured on medicine both at Paris and Montpellier in the opening years of the century, has left little beyond a few recipes preserved in manuscripts at Oxford (Bod. MS. 786, fos. 170–1) and Cambridge (Peterhouse MS. 222, fol. 10), though other works by him of a theological nature are known. He was later in attendance on Isabella, sister of Henry III, in a medical capacity, and appears to have cured both Bishop Grosseteste and the Earl of Gloucester of the effects of poison. Like many others of this period he is remembered more for his relationships with the great than for any creative contribution to the science of medicine.

Sometimes confused with John of St Giles is John of St Albans. He was on the medical staff of Richard I of England during the third crusade, where he cured Philip Augustus of France of fever, but not before the king had lost his hair and his nails. About 1234 he succeeded Edmund of Abingdon, later Archbishop of Canterbury, as treasurer of Salisbury. Also at Salisbury was Thomas of Eblesburne, a canon who practised medicine, and who has left a recipe now preserved in MS. Royal 12 B. xii.

More important than any of these was John of Toledo, a Cistercian who in 1243 became Cardinal. The name 'Toledo' suggests that he had studied in Spain and perhaps acquired his medical knowledge there. He was physician to Pope Innocent IV, whom he attended in his last illness. Accusations against him that he dabbled in astrology, necromancy and alchemy appear to have no foundations, though his scientific investigations may well have drawn these complaints on his head, as they did for his contemporary Roger Bacon.

John, known as Cardinalis Albus because of his white Cistercian habit, does not appear to have practised in this country. He wrote several works of which perhaps the *De regimine sanitatis* was the most popular. His advice is sensible and conservative. He speaks of exercise, temperance in eating, drinking and sleeping, the kinds of food one should eat, meat, fish, and vegetables. His estimation of fruit is low, because it produces bad humours which putrefy easily and cause fevers: but fruit may be taken as a medicine, such as prunes and cherries in summer, pears after food because they help digestion, nuts because they counteract poison, and figs and grapes. Wine should be drunk with water, otherwise the brain is filled with vapours. In bed one should first sleep on the right side, then on the left and finally turn over on to the right side. Certain laxatives such as mirobolani and triphera should always be at hand.

Blood letting should be done at regular times, in spring to get rid of excess humours, in autumn to get rid of the 'malice' of humours. Besides this, bloodletting is necessary for the cure of various blains and abscesses, accompanied by medicines, called repercussive and maturative, which suppress poisonous matter or bring it to the surface. Bathing is also recommended, but it should not be done for at least an hour after a meal. Baths are advised not merely for the sake of cleanliness but as a general matter of good health, but they should not be taken too hot otherwise they might lead to weakness of heart and limbs or even to a stroke. The final section, which was often treated as a separate work, deals with poisons, relating mainly to bites from snakes, scorpions and mad dogs. His treatment for these consists mainly in causing a vomit, bleeding three days later from the hepatic vein and a final bath three days later. This treatise, unpretentious as it may seem, had a wide circulation and manuscripts of it can be found in most European libraries. It was published by Julius Pagel in 1907. Other works are also attributed to John of Toledo, one dealing with alchemy, the other an *Ars memorandi,* but on what evidence is not clear. Arnold of Villanova had great respect for his skill and judgement and recommended two of his remedies.

The royal physicians were obviously men of great medical skill, but few have left any evidence of their competence. Of the names recorded in royal documents, Ralph Besace, Henry of Campeden, Nigel of Miridene, Ralph Necton, Reginald of Bath, Robert of St Albans, Thomas of Essex, William of Fécamp, and several others, none is connected with writings of any kind. Roger Lacock is known to have composed prescriptions, of which one, an ointment for eyes made from fennel, rue, musk and attic honey and accompanied with full instructions for its confection and application, is preserved in Royal MS. 12 B. xii. But that is all. Nicholas of Farnham, professor of medicine at Bologna, later professor of theology at Paris, and eventually Bishop of Durham, may have composed some medical treatises, but those attributed to him by John Bale belong to other writers, such as Nicholas of Salerno and Bartholomaeus. If he, in fact, wrote a *Practica medicine* and a work *De viribus herbarum* they do not appear to have survived, whilst a commentary on Galen, preserved in the Bibliothèque Nationale, lat. MS. 7015, and ascribed to Nicholas de Anglia cannot be shown with any certainty to be his.

On the whole, therefore, little progress was made during the course of the century and the doctrine prevalent among the Salernitans continued to be followed. Physiology, in accordance with Galenic tradition, was based on teleology and the doctrine of organic forces, namely, motive, vital, nutritive and generative, linked with the four organs, brain, heart, liver and testicles. Pathology was founded on the doctrine of the four humours, diagnosis being made by observing the disturbances of functions, chiefly by examination of the pulse and urine, the pulse showing the condition of the heart, the urine the condition of the liver. In therapeutics the chief aim was to regulate the manner of life and nourishment of the patient by hygiene and diet; but general treatment included venesection, mild aperients and an armoury of drugs.

Whether or not the physicians of the time deserved the attacks made on them by Roger Bacon is doubtful, for the basis of his arguments only concerns medicine as he conceived it, and his conception of it was biased by his study of subjects not wholly akin to medicine. He says that the ordinary doctor knows nothing about simple drugs and has to trust himself to apothecaries who are ignorant or deceitful, for they cheat the physicians both as regards the quality of drugs and their price. They are also ignorant of compound drugs, for besides knowing nothing about the relation of noxious drugs to the human body, they do not understand how to compound them in correct proportions, how to ferment them or how to ensure that one drug will counteract another. All this seems fair enough. But he then proceeds to berate them for more doubtful deficiencies. He accuses them of not pursuing the study of astrology, for he is of the opinion that laxative drugs, phlebotomy and the whole medical system is affected by atmospheric changes brought about by the movements of the heavens and the stars. He accuses them of being ignorant of alchemy and agriculture and of knowing nothing of natural philosophy, 'for Aristotle says, that where natural philosophy ends, there medicine begins, since natural philosophy provides the first principles of health and sickness'. Furthermore they are ignorant of metaphysics. But perhaps they can be excused because ordinary students have no other books but the works of Aristotle and few understand them, 'for these sciences have been taught for only twenty years or so', and the translations they use are faulty 'since an infinite number of lines, and even of whole chapters are omitted, as can be proved by comparing them with the Greek originals'. He accuses the physicians also of making gross blunders and failing to investigate the causes of disease and their treatment by experiment. 'But this is not to be wondered at, since it is dangerous to experiment on the human body, and far from easy.' Scientists in other fields can experiment on inanimate objects and test their results until all faults and errors are eliminated. But doctors are not able to do this because of the dignity and superiority of the material they are dealing with. 'And since truth cannot be reached except by experimentation perhaps doctors should be excused if they make more mistakes than other experimental scientists.' He attributes many of the mistakes to their reliance on Avicenna, whose diagnoses are not always sound. 'Rhases puts the diagnosis of diseases among the first duties of a practitioner, so that the causes and symptoms of any kind of illness can be clearly recognized.' But even if the doctors were correct in their diagnosis of disease, they would still lack knowledge of drugs or even the drugs themselves.

In this diatribe, only part of which is justifiable, Bacon repeats himself interminably and, in spite of his assumption of superior knowledge, knows little of drugs himself. In the course of this piece he mentions about eighty of them; but it is noticeable that when he records his personal experience, he recurs more often than not to rhubarb as a kind of panacea. His acquaintance with medical writers, however, is fairly wide, and he quotes no fewer than seventeen authors, eight of whom are Arabs. On the whole, Bacon overstates his case and had he attacked someone of the stature of Gilbertus Anglicus, he would have been put firmly in his place.

Sometime before 1260 Bartholomaeus Anglicus, a Franciscan friar, though not a medical man by profession or training, wrote an encyclopaedia, *De proprietatibus rerum*, the aim of which was to assist readers in understanding the difficulties that arise in the study of sacred scripture. His compilation ranges over a vast number of subjects, but the one pertinent to our theme is medicine. Though there are numerous passages throughout the encyclopaedia referring to medical topics, the seventh book expressly deals with diseases. In true medieval fashion he begins with diseases of the head and continues with those that affect other members of the body down to the feet. Most of his ideas are derived from Constantine the African whom he quotes in almost every one of the seventy chapters, but he omits the long lists of remedies found in other medical treatises of the day. In the fourth and fifth chapters he deals with frenzy and mental disturbance, chapters which, when published some years ago, attracted a great deal of attention. It was not considered possible that anyone in the Middle Ages should have gained so firm a grasp of this complex subject: and yet no surprise should have been expressed at all, since most of the material was taken from Constantine, who himself had borrowed it from late classical and Byzantine writers. Besides these purely medical topics, gout, arthritis, ulcers, fevers and so on, there are chapters on physiology, on pulse, bloodletting, child care, food, diet: in short, a complete summary of the medical and hygienic knowledge available at that time.

Chapter Seven

Surgery

Unlike the work of the physicians, which in the thirteenth century made no apparent progress, the work of surgery went forward at an exhilarating pace. After the first Bamberg surgery, which is but a compilation from previous texts, the book by Roger of Salerno opened up great possibilities. Written, as it says in the prologue, 'for our associates, in order that they may retain and have in writing the knowledge which they have gained from us in our practice', the book was severely practical, eliminating all those passages concerning theory, such as the humours, phlebotomy and so on, which had been an essential part of the Bamberg text. It had an immediate success and exerted a wide and abiding influence. It was re-worked, amplified, commented on and excerpted for more than a hundred years. Even in the earliest manuscripts the margins are full of notes, interlinear glosses and personal anecdotes, showing how useful and how well used this book was. We do not know exactly when it was written, but in 1170, when Guido of Arezzo, a professor of logic, and Roger's pupil, put the material into a more logical order, some of Roger's students were still alive and Guido considered it necessary to exculpate himself for having rearranged things in a way different from his master's method of teaching.

The work is divided into four books. The first deals with wounds in the head, most of which seem to have been caused by arrows, swords and other weapons of aggression, a vivid comment on the times: but he treats of other conditions as well, such as tinea, scrofula, sore gums, toothache, luxation of the jaw, pustules on the face and worms in the ears. For mania and melancholy he advised making an incision in the head in the form of a cross 'in order that the humours may escape to the exterior'. In the second book he deals with the neck, not merely wounds, but boils, quinsy, scrofula. The third treats of wounds 'we consider to be fatal, and therefore it is better to leave them alone lest the patient seems to die through our fault'. The fourth book is devoted to wounds of the lower limbs, but it strays from its purpose and also deals with leprosy, alopecia and burns.

Roger's practical experience is revealed on every page of this treatise. He deals extensively with wounds of the skull, indicates when suitable surgical intervention is necessary in brain injury, gives instructions for differential diagnosis of the lesions of bones and distinguishes those cases in which it is advisable to trephine. The technique of trephining is accurately described: a series of small holes should first be made with the trephine so that bony fragments may be raised without damage to the meninges. For treatment of wounds of the intestine and peritoneum, he advises that if the viscera are protruding and have been exposed to the air, thereby growing cold, the belly of an animal should be opened and placed on the injured part to impart warmth and softness. Afterwards the intestines should be cleansed with a warm sponge, replaced in the abdomen, and the wound left open until normal functioning of the intestine can be observed. Into the edges of the wound lint should be introduced to permit drainage and the bandage should be changed every day. For the treatment of fractures and dislocations his instructions are precise and detailed. He also described operations for lithotomy, hydrocele and hernia, though strangely enough he does not include any mention of the truss which had been counselled and advised in the Bamberg surgery in the following words:

If a patient does not wish to undergo treatment by extraction of the member and by cautery, the hernia may be thus reduced. A mould is made of clay in the form of a shield with a hole in the middle. Melted lead is then poured into it so that it takes the form of the mould: when it has cooled, it should be taken from the mould and put on the ground, where it is gently pounded with a blunt hammer and pared with shears. It should then be sewn between two bands, as if in a bag, and when it is ready a plaster of *apostolicon* is put on the skin and the shield-shaped apparatus is applied, so that one of the bands hangs downward and passed between the buttocks. The ends are then tied over the kidneys. During sleep it may be removed and fastened on again in the morning.

This kind of truss had been known for centuries and examples of it, from the fifth to the eighth centuries, have been discovered in northern France.

Some of Roger's pages are devoted to interesting diagnostic observations, such as that on stones in the bladder and prostatic hypertrophy. Surgical treatment of cancer of the rectum and of the uterus is pronounced possible, but he advises against it on account of the inherent danger in such operations and the high percentage of failure. One of the notable omissions from Roger's book is any mention of the soporific sponge which had appeared in the Bamberg surgery. Though this had been known from the ninth century at least, it had only been included previously in manuals of pharmacy; but its inclusion in a book on surgery shows that operations were not so barbaric in the twelfth century as they were later to become. The chief ingredients were opium, hyosciamus, mandragora, ground ivy, lettuce juice and hemlock. A sponge was soaked in these drugs, allowed to dry, and then moistened in warm water and applied to the nostrils of the patient just before the operation. Though the efficacy of such means has been doubted by later investigators, it would appear that some results must have been obtained by this method, otherwise the practice would not have been continued, as it was, for so long.

Roger's work, though showing much personal experience, was based essentially on the various translations of Constantine, particularly on the ninth book of the *Practica* of the *Pantegni*, and was therefore an amalgam of Eastern and Byzantine medicine, showing all the typical characteristics of south Italian medicine, that is, a mixture of Latin, Greek and Arabic sources. Between 1170, when Guido of Arezzo remodelled Roger's material, and 1187, some new and most important surgical texts were translated by Gerard of Cremona from the Arabic: namely, Rhases, three surgical tractates of Albucasis and the *Canon* of Avicenna. Though these were ultimately based on the same Greek sources as the work of Roger, they were not so brief, nor so rigidly practical as the Salernitan text, and they enabled the new generation of surgeons and teachers of surgery to enlarge the boundaries of their knowledge. The use of these new texts did not become apparent immediately, and Avicenna seems to have been the first to be put under contribution.

The use of Avicenna was revealed in the glosses of Roland of Parma, who was teaching and practising at Bologna about the same time as Hugh of Lucca. Hugh had been summoned to the city in 1214 and been employed at a salary of 600 *Bolognini* a year. His contract laid down that he must remain in the city for at least six months every year and that in time of war he was to give his services to the army. When the Bolognese took part in the fifth crusade he accompanied the soldiers to Egypt, took part in the siege of Damietta and in 1212 returned home where he continued to look after the citizens, reporting on wounded persons in both a surgical and legal capacity. A statute of the time laid down that he was bound to treat everyone, except those suffering from hernia, at certain fees fixed according to the social status of the patient. He was, therefore, a highly skilled and experienced surgeon. As Hugh left no writings it is not possible to say whether the new Arabic texts had any influence on his ideas, but the little we know of his work (through Theodoric, his son) points to a man of practice rather than erudition. Roland, on the other hand, was a teacher. In the second part of his book Roland apologizes for his discursive method:

Let no one accuse me of prolixity or crude style, for often brevity leads to obscurity rather than to compendiousness. I write not only for those who are already proficient, but also for others. And therefore whatever I heard either in public or private from the admirable doctor [Roger] and whatever I have been able to glean from his writings, I have put into order, so that his ideas may more clearly be grasped.

This seems to imply that Roger's treatise was addressed, not to students, but to experienced surgeons, and that it was couched in succinct phrases because it presupposed a great deal of knowledge in the reader. Roland, who was writing for students, felt the need to expand this terse record and to fill in the gaps which caused difficulty to the novice. He pretended also to be an experienced surgeon and attributed to himself an operation on the lung which, in fact, had been performed by Hugh in his presence. His work, written not before 1230, perhaps not even before 1240, shows no originality, although in some chapters he put forward his own views, for example on the cure of tinea, cicatrization of nerves, wounds in the veins, and cures for apostemes. From his book we get a good idea of the type of surgical instruments available to him : trephine, great and small, scalpels, razors, spatulae, curved and straight pincers, coarse, fine and square needles, dilators, means for draining wounds and numerous varieties of instruments for cautery.

The glosses of the Four Masters on the text of Roland and Roger, though attributed to four Salernitans, Archimatteus, Petrocellus, Platearius and Ferrarius, are really the product of the school of Bologna. This false attribution, taken together with the known rivalry between Hugh of Lucca and Roland, points to a shifting of importance from Salerno to the North. None of the four Salernitans mentioned was alive when Roger finished his book on surgery nor were some of the Arabic texts quoted in the glosses available to the teachers at Salerno. They could not, therefore, have written a gloss on Roger's text. Though the new movement in medicine had been initiated at Salerno, its progress was to be associated with the towns of the north, and in future Bologna, Padua, Verona, Venice and Milan were to be the nurseries of surgeons.

The commentary of the Four Masters opens with a kind of *apologia*: 'Many books have been written on medicine and diet by many people, but on surgery few or practically none at all. And so Master Roland, at the instance of his fellows and friends, wrote this book to remedy the lack of treatises on surgery.' Even on the first page of this commentary we find quotations from Isaac Judaeus, Constantine, John Afflacius, Galen; and gradually the names of Avicenna, Aristotle, Rhases, Albucasis and Serapion begin to appear. This commentary does not add much to the basic doctrines of Roger, except in certain details such as the healing of cut sinews, and is merely an amplification of the text, probably for teaching purposes.

There was, however, in the south of France, at Montpellier, a more important follower of the Salernitan tradition. He was William de Congenis,

a married man, well educated, greatly experienced and of good reputation. To him all the sick who had been neglected by other surgeons
came, from all parts of the world, East and West, North and South,
and even the Arabs respected him. The regent masters in the chairs
of medicine were not ashamed to quote him in support of their teaching during his lifetime. And so I call him *Lord* and *Master*, since the
title *Master* has sunk so low at Montpellier that even a donkey driver
is called Master. Master William gave lectures to the University
students at least twice a year, at Christmas and Easter, when all other
lectures finished. Now this was his method of teaching. He had the
book on surgery by Roger before him, but instead of merely repeat-
ing the text, he followed the order of chapters and showed how he
himself operated, sometimes approving of what Roger said, at other
times changing it for something better, and sometimes even discarding it, as contrary to ordinary surgical practice.

All this is related by his pupil, himself a former student at Paris and Bologna. He reports William's teaching in his own glosses on William's text, so that we have a vivid picture of what surgical teaching and practice was like at Montpellier in the first half of the thirteenth century. The dates for this teaching are fixed by William's having been physician and surgeon to Simon de Mont-fort, who died 1218. Instruction was not merely verbal, but prac-tical. The students were taken to the hospital of the Holy Spirit at Montpellier and taught there 'not merely listening but watching, because only in this way can the student obtain full comprehension of operating, and besides this he gets courage, because in surgery boldness is an essential'. So they watched operations on the head, intestines and other internal organs: 'and once when the Master was trephining a wounded man, one of the students fainted as soon as he saw the brain moving; so my advice is that no one should attempt any operation until he has seen it done'. Unlike other medical writers of the times William and his pupil did not condemn or disdain the itinerant surgeons. They realized that surgery was a practical art gained by experience and not necessarily dependent on books. For such operations as removal of cataract they readily accepted that these specialists were often more skilled than the medical practitioner or the general surgeon.

> At Montpellier in New Street, I saw one of these men operating on Otto de Stadio for cataract. He operated skilfully, but he was not successful, for, as he said to me, the cataract was not mature enough to be couched. But take note that these surgeons, who move about from place to place, are often more skilful than famous surgeons because of their constant practice. All the same, before they acquire this skill, they do much damage. Even William did not always find these operations easy.

> I saw Master William incising the eye-lids of one of the students and making heavy weather of it. First he cut and then he sewed it and he made a continuous suture, on which he placed red powder. But because it had tired him, we asked him to desist for that day. On the third day when the suture was removed, the student said that it hurt him more than the incision. When the other eye had to be treated, we dare not ask the Master to do it, because the student was poor, and what he had done previously, he had done freely at our request.

The pupil goes on to say that this experience stimulated him into finding a simpler way of doing this operation, and later, when he reached Paris, he had a special instrument made with which he operated on both eyes of one of his friends, a canon of Höxter in Westphalia.

Some of the wounds and fractures that William dealt with were by no means simple, and we read of rupture of the peritoneum, wounds in the liver, strangury, hernia, dislocation of the jugular vertebrae, fistula *prope anum* and many others. For hernia he recommended a truss: 'this is most convenient and useful, especially for those who are heavy eaters, because it prevents the intestines from falling down and weighing heavily on the other organs'. Even men who did not suffer from hernia wore one as a precaution, particularly when they put on heavy armour and indulged in strenuous exercise. In cases of dislocation of the vertebrae in the neck he advised the patient to lie down on the ground or on a bench: 'Then heavy blows are administered to the sole of the foot, and this puts the bone back in place. The knights of Provence, who often suffer from this on account of their tournaments, always do this to one another when it happens.' For scrofula William used realgar 'and at Montpellier this was the traditional treatment', but the pupil warns surgeons against using it (for it was a corrosive) unless they knew an antidote. On wounds of the liver, he advised the surgeon not to tamper with them: 'but you should tell the patient's friends that it may be fatal. But if the friends do not wish the patient to die without something having been attempted by the surgeon, demand a high fee, so that if you suffer the shame of seeing your operation unsuccessful, at least you will not suffer any financial loss.' On the other hand, William was not mercenary: 'These are the good and inexpensive ointments for those who cannot go to great expense for where the surgeon cannot earn money, at least he can obtain friends without doing them any damage.'

On tinea he has a rather interesting social comment:

Often well-bred and rich people are found to suffer from this, because their mothers have lived in idleness and bred superfluous humours with which the child is born when it is conceived in the womb. . . . It is quite otherwise with the children of the peasants and the poor, who are always born beautiful, even though afterwards, through excessive labour and neglect of hygiene, they become ugly.

Evidently the treatment of this disease was tedious to medical men, for William says that if the cure should be undertaken he should have the fee paid first, so that his labours are sweetened.

We have in these two, William and his pupil, excellent witnesses to the diffusion of Roger's text and to the interest in surgical improvements to which it gave rise. William's pupil, as his reference to Höxter shows, later practised in Germany, where, no doubt, he imparted the knowledge acquired at Paris, Bologna and Montpellier to his countrymen. This fact alone should contradict the sneers of Guy de Chauliac, made in the following century, that the Teutons put all their faith in prayers, herbs and incantations. Nothing could be more rational and practical than this text, written about 1250 in Germany, embodying the teaching and experience of the four greatest medical centres in Europe.

Other Roger glosses are found in an Italian manuscript of the end of the thirteenth century: Bibl. Vallicelliana Codex C 102, written apparently by a religious: 'I, a sinner, but by the grace of God, a member of a religious order.' The book is written for the use of other religious persons in order that they may treat the poor for nothing, since they are abandoned by the ordinary physicians and surgeons; but from the rich they are to receive fees. He speaks of a certain Frater R. de Boemonte, a Dominican friar, 'who for a long time studied medicine'. As mention is made elsewhere in the manuscript of Normannia, the author may be a Frenchman. He quotes William de Congenis several times, but also gives recipes which he learned from women practitioners and women apothecaries, 'cyrurgica, apotecaria, filia apotecarii'.

That Roger's text on surgery reached even farther north to Iceland and Denmark can be inferred both from surviving literature and from evidence of surgical practice. The Icelandic book of law, Grágásand, makes explicit mention of an object which served to probe and ascertain the depth of a wound. The word used, *keri*, is a literal translation of the Salernitan *tenta*, first employed to designate a vegetable laminaria put into a fistula to enlarge it, and adopted by Roger to denote a removable plug inserted into the wounds to keep them open and allow free drainage. The classification of wounds also in this law-book follows Roger's method, and the calculation of fines for wounds inflicted was based on whether the wound was located in the head, upper or lower cavity of the body, whether it reached the bone marrow and so on. The treatment of fractures can also be traced to Roger's treatise. In Denmark, the numerous skeletons found at the Cistercian abbey of Øm numbering several hundreds and comprising men, women and children (indicating that there was a hospital attached to the monastery), all show traces of the application of Salernitan surgery. Whilst most of the skeletons show that the wounds were inflicted by sharp instruments, such as swords, there are skulls with clear evidence of trephining. These are particularly revealing, for in many cases the growth of the bone anterior to the death of the patient shows that these operations were highly successful. Most of the fractures in arms, legs and collar bones had also healed before death intervened, a remarkable tribute both to the surgical knowledge and practice of the monks and of their medical assistants.

For England we do not possess such striking evidence of the diffusion of Roger's teaching on surgery. We know that such texts existed at Christ Church, Canterbury, but since the catalogue of books represents only what was in the library during Henry Eastry's term of office (1284–1331) we cannot infer that they were used by the monks much earlier. James' supposition that the John of London (who bequeathed nearly eighty books to Christchurch, of which twenty-three are medical, several of them surgical, including that of Roger) cannot possibly be the disciple of Roger Bacon, who was sent to Pope Clement in 1267, is well founded; for among his books are some, such as those by Lanfranc and Bernard Gordon, which were not finished until the opening years of the fourteenth century. There is, however, one detail which may indicate that Roger's surgery was known and used in thirteenth century England: this is MS. Bodley 553, written in France in the first half of the thirteenth century and presented much later to the library. This contains the text of William de Congenis, another copy of which was amongst John of London's books.

The breaking of the Salernitan tradition in Bologna is due to Bruno Longoburgo in whose work Albucasis was used extensively for the first time. Bruno came from Calabria, where he had been trained, to Padua, where, at the request of Andrea di Vicenza, he wrote his book on surgery; later he made an abridgement of it and dedicated it to Lazaro di Padua. He was a learned scholar rather than a skilled surgeon and his book was based more on authorities than on his personal experience. In the prologue to his work he admits that his purpose was to make a compilation from the writings of others, and to amplify this by details provided by reasoning and experience. The sources he used were Hippocrates (the *Aphorisms*), Constantine, Rhases (the *Almansor*), Avicenna, Haly Abbas, and Albucasis; but he also used Galen in translations which were not those of either Constantine or Gerard of Cremona. This text superseded Roger as the basis of teaching in Bologna, so that the surgical school of that city was founded on Hugh of Lucca's experience and Bruno's erudition.

Theodoric, son of Hugh, was to take advantage of both. He had been brought to Bologna in 1214 when his father was appointed surgeon to the city, and, together with his three brothers, Hubert, Veltro and Francis, had been taught medicine, as was the custom, by his father. He eventually joined the Dominicans, became penitentiary to the Pope (probably Innocent IV), was appointed Bishop of Bitonto about 1262, and Bishop of Cervia in 1266. In spite of these religious obligations he always resided in Bologna, exercised his profession as physician and surgeon there, and as a result amassed great riches, which he bequeathed to his church and his Order at his death in 1298. Unlike his father he wrote a *Chirurgia magna* in which he recorded Hugh's experience and his own practice. It was written at the request of the Bishop of Valencia in Spain. Much of it is borrowed from Bruno Longoburgo, and indeed all the authors quoted by Theodoric are found in Bruno. But he names two others not mentioned by Bruno, namely Roger and Roland, the latter of whom had spoken in derogatory terms of the Bolognese surgeons. Theodoric had read their works and took it upon himself to answer them. Theodoric accuses them of stupidity and error on the question of healing wounds:

> They and their disciples teach, and almost all modern surgeons follow them, that pus should be generated in wounds. There could be no greater error than this. For it does nothing else but hinder the work of nature, prolong the disease, prevent healing and the closing up of wounds.

'My father,' he says in another passage, 'used to heal almost every kind of wound with wine alone, and he produced the most beautiful cicatrization without any ointment.' This was a good disinfectant, because it contained alcohol and tartrates. Simple as this method was, it showed tremendous progress on all that had gone before and was one of the greatest contributions to surgery. On other matters also he showed fine common sense and a critical appraisement born of long experience: 'I say this, that in medicine the essential thing is the ingenuity and alertness of the physician, for when unusual accidents occur, he should know how to lessen or increase the strength of the medicine, otherwise he will fall into error.' On the extraction of arrows he remarked: 'The methods employed for extracting arrows cannot be described in detail, for every day we see new instruments and new methods being invented by clever and ingenious physicians.' On fractures and dislocations he himself showed considerable ingenuity and he described the evidence for shoulder dislocation (known as the Dugas sign and considered, in 1857, to be a new principle of diagnosis) in the following words: 'When the humerus is dislocated, the signs are: a concavity near the point of the shoulder, marked fullness of the armpit and *inability to touch the opposite ear with the hands.*'

Theodoric, although conscious of having borrowed much from others, was aware that he had made valuable contributions to surgery, and at the end of his book he added these words:

I have not put anything into this book which I have not tested, for I did not wish my work to contain more of other men's ideas than my own. For it would be useless to bring out a new book if equally good or better ideas could be found in other books. I have also striven to be brief, for I do not wish to make my book tedious to read.

Contemporary with Theodoric was William of Saliceto, a native of Piacenza. He was not a surgeon pure and simple, but a physician and a cleric. He wrote his book in 1275 whilst he was the city surgeon of Verona. In the dedication to Bono del Garbo, son-in-law of Taddeo Alderotti, he said: 'My purpose is to compose a book on manual operation to satisfy both you and your companions ... according to the knowledge I have gained through long years of experience and to give example of what I have done with my own hands.' The book lives up to this promise. He gives no quotations at all from other authors and always supports his teaching by describing operations he himself had carried out. Yet his work is more complete and detailed than Roger, Roland, Bruno and Theodoric put together. Though it is obvious that he had learned from Rhases, Albucasis, Avicenna and Mesue, he always thought for himself, criticizing his contemporaries and preferring his own knowledge to outworn traditions. Furthermore he wrote clearly and elegantly and without any scholastic argument. From the first page, one is conscious of a man who had been educated at a university, had put his theory into practice on the battlefield, had made a reputation in various cities in Lombardy by treating rich and poor alike, visiting hospitals and prisons, and had crowned his career by teaching for four years at Bologna, finally ending his life in the service of the city of Verona. He relates cures effected by him at Cremona, Piacenza, Bergamo, Pavia and elsewhere: 'I saw a prisoner at Cremona who stabbed himself in the lung through desperation... I cured him.' 'I saw a soldier at Bergamo... and with my own hands I extracted the arrow, and he was perfectly cured and lived a long time afterwards, and I got a good fee for it. I cured a man at Pavia de Predela, named John, who struck himself with a knife in the belly and all his intestines fell out.... Ottobonus of Pavia was called to him and seeing the intestines outside the body said he was dead. But wishing to put the intestines back into place he was unable to do it... and he came to me, accompanied by the friends of the patient whilst I was in the Communal Palace.' William cured him 'and I continued treatment with Master Ottobonus, and after the man was cured he married, had children and lived for a long time'. William describes other cases, some of them treated with the assistance of other surgeons, whom he calls 'magistri manuales'.

At the end of the book William gives the exact year and day when he completed its composition: 'on the eighth of June in the city of Verona, where I was staying, for I was receiving a salary from the commune; but I had lectured on the subject at Bologna for four years previously; and from the nature of the material and its arrangement it will make any one who studies it *a good surgeon and a good physician.*' This latter remark shows that, at least in Italy, medicine and surgery were not separated. Indeed, William was both surgeon and physician, and at the instance of Ruffino, Prior of S. Ambrogio at Piacenza, he wrote a *Summa conservationis et curationis* for the benefit of his son, Leonardino, whom he had brought up in the profession of medicine. Both his works were to have lasting influence not only in Italy, but also in France and England.

A contemporary, and perhaps an acquaintance of William of

Saliceto was William of Brescia. From 1274 to 1279 he taught logic at Padua; he then went to Bologna where he was a pupil of Taddeo Alderotti, by whom he was granted a doctorate. Later he became physician to Pope Boniface VIII (1294), who conferred on him a canonry at Paris, one at Constance, and finally one at Lincoln. Clement V (1305) and John XXII (1316) both appointed him as their physician. In 1326 he found himself at Paris and there he drew up a plan for a college to be erected at Bologna in which two students of canon law, two of medicine, four in arts and philology were to reside; it was called Collegium Brescianum after him, and was united with the Gregorianum by Eugene IV in 1437. He died soon after 1326. He wrote a *Practica ad unamquamque egritudinem a capite ad pedes*, and some tracts, *De febribus, De peste, De consilio observando tempore pestilentiali, De cura pestis*, all of which were printed in 1508 and 1515; in the book he gives himself the title *Aggregator*. He also wrote *De memoria* and a number of *Consilia* which have not been printed. Henri de Mondeville wrote his surgery at William of Brescia's request, 'at the request and command of a professor in the science of medicine, formerly the physician of Popes Boniface and Benedict, and at present in the service of Pope Clement the Fifth....' William of Brescia came to England and was a great friend of Winchelsey, Archbishop of Canterbury, who helped him in his struggle to obtain his canonry at Lincoln. It is not known whether Brescia practised here or not, but it seems unlikely.

William of Saliceto's teaching was carried to France by Lanfrank, one of his pupils, who was driven from Milan by the Visconti. Like William, Lanfranc was a cleric and also a physician and surgeon. Lanfranc went first to Lyons where he stayed for a time and wrote, at the request of his friend Bernard, his *Chirurgia parva*. His ambition was to write a larger work, but the necessity to provide for himself and the education of his son, besides the demands of his practice, detained him in the provinces until 1295, when he set out for Paris. There he was invited by Jean de Passavant, dean of the faculty of Medicine, and some of his associates to give lectures on surgery, and probably as a result he was able to complete his *Chirurgia magna* in 1296.

Lanfranc's surgery owes a great deal to his master William of Saliceto, but he quotes his authorities more frequently than William. He was widely read and his sources include Hippocrates, Galen, Aristotle, Alexander, from classical times; Hunain, Isaac Judaeus, Rhases, Haly Abbas, Avicenna, John, son of Mesue, Serapion, Albucasis and Averroes from among the Arabs; Constantine, Copho, Platearius, Giovanni di San Paolo, Maurus, Roger and Roland from the Salernitans, besides Theodoric, William of Saliceto and a certain William de Somiris (this last may be William of Sumere whose *parvus viaticus* is found in two manuscripts at Cambridge and London (CCC MS. 279 and B.M. Royal 12 E. xxxiii)). Thus Lanfranc brought all the treasures of Italian surgery into France at one swoop. Lanfranc was, in general, averse to using the knife and wherever possible he advised the use of medicines, styptics and cautery, but he records many of his cases in which he used both lancet and razor. His experience had been that many surgeons operated without due knowledge and care and patients were put in extreme danger. He mentions several times that his advice had not been followed by patients who had been persuaded by unskilled surgeons and though the results were not always fatal they fell into worse straits. Lanfranc was always moderate, sound and full of common sense, and quite uninfluenced by the rigid scholastic approach which characterised his contemporary, Henri de Mondeville.

Mondeville was a cleric, who had evidently studied philosophy and knew some theology. He disdained lay practitioners and was so conscious of his dignity as a surgeon that he did not hesitate to place himself in the same rank as a physician. Besides having studied under Pitard, he had travelled about a great deal with the armies and acquired great experience. He had given lectures at Montpellier, only leaving it to become surgeon to Phillippe le Bel. In 1306 he began to write his treatise and had completed two books by 1312 when he was called away to Arras and then to England in the train of Charles de Valois, the King's brother. He forsook his studies, his lectures, his book, hoping to receive the money he was owed by the King, but having wasted his time he came back to resume his writing. He was prevented from making great progress by the crowds of clients who came to see him, and by the insistence of his students, so that he could not write more than one line a day on average. He illustrated his book with thirteen drawings of anatomy, which according to the captions given to them must have been extremely instructive and indeed epoch-making; but since they were afterwards copied by artists with no knowledge of surgery or physical anatomy, the series that has been preserved, apart from being too small for usefulness, provides no more than formal likenesses. Mondeville never finished his book because he died, having suffered for a long time, as he tells us, from phthisis. The great value of Mondeville's book, acknowledged even by Guy de Chauliac, lies in its straightforward and brusque expression of opinion. His views on the ethics of the medical profession are as biting as they are honest. And though he appears to be venal, one must take into account that he had served the King of France for long periods without receiving any remuneration. His comments, therefore, on fees should be seen in this light. Mondeville was immensely well equipped for his task. Besides his varied experience, he had studied all the accepted authorities, of whom he quotes no less than 59, ranging from Hippocrates to his contemporaries. The first book deals with anatomy, derived in the main from Avicenna. This is followed by a discussion on the professional, technical and social problems of the surgeon in general. It is here that he points out the futility of separating surgery from medicine and takes the physicians to task for either employing ignorant barbers to do their surgical work in order that they may keep the authority, or disdaining surgeons altogether.

The second book deals with wounds and ulcers, and here he recounts the troubles he and Pitard encountered in trying to bring the new methods of Theodoric of Cervia into French medical practice. He includes seventeen methods for the arrest of haemorrhage.

The third book deals with special surgery, arranged in three parts: the first discusses incisions, cauterisation, bleeding, amputation, embalming, cutaneous eruptions and leprosy. The second is concerned with humours and abscesses; the third deals with diseases in various members. Tract V is an antidotarium (the fourth book having been omitted through ill health) which deals with the properties of medicinal substances used in surgery.

Though Bernard de Gordon, who was a contemporary of Mondeville, was not *ex professo* a surgeon and therefore does not belong to this section, his work must be dealt with at this stage in order that full appreciation can be given to the English writers of the same period. From the colophon of his work, we know that Gordon began his *Lilium medicine* in July 1303 after he had been lecturing at Montpellier for twenty years. He tells us in the same place that he had already written four other works: the *Tractatus super regimen acutorum*, finished in 1294; the *Tractatus super prognostica sive de crisi et diebus criticis*, finished 25 January 1295; the *De ingeniis curandorum morborum*, July 1299; and the *Tractatus de gradibus*, 1303. This was by no means the end of his literary activity, for in 1308 he compiled a *Liber de conservatione vitae humanae*, consisting of four parts, *de phlebotomia, de urinis, de pulsibus,* and *de conservatione vitae humanae*. A great number of other works attributed to him still remain unedited. All his writings were popular and most of them were translated into French, Spanish, German and Hebrew.

Gordon was long thought to be a Scotsman, but there is nothing in his writings to bear this out. The title which he gave to his book may even indicate that he was French: for he explains that 'in a lily there are many flowers; and in each flower there are three petals with six golden stamens. In the same way this book contains seven parts.' The three petals probably refer to the Fleur de Lys of France: certainly they could not describe the Thistle of Scotland. When Gaddesden wrote his own book on medicine he imitated Gordon by entitling it *Rosa medicinae*, and was obviously referring to the Rose of England.

Unlike most of the writers of the time Gordon indulges in few personal reminiscences, but here and there a topical allusion occurs. On scorpions, for instance, he says: 'They are found not far from here at Avignon.' On scrophula he says: 'And if they are not cured, let them go to the King, for kings are accustomed to cure solely by touch, and this applies particularly to the kings of France.' On leprosy he is perfectly honest about his inability to cure it. He says a man can be leprous even though no signs show in the face, for he knew a man whose hands and feet only were affected. He had seen a man like this for twenty years and when he was brought before Gordon for judgement, whether to be banished or not, Gordon let him go. 'But whether that was right or not, God knows.' He recalls the case of a certain countess who came to Montpellier to be cured by him. 'And a certain bachelor of medicine looked after her and after he had lain with her and made her pregnant, he became a perfect leper.' Gordon was interested in surgery also. He followed Theodoric on the care of wounds and would not allow anything to be put on them before they were sewn up. For a broken limb he gave this advice:

> Let the leg or arm be placed in a ship-like vessel and bound up so that it cannot be broken again by sudden movement, since this happens sometimes in sleep: hang a rope over the bed so that when the patient wants to move some part of his body he can lift himself up: and let there be a hole in the bed so that he can relieve himself, othewise it might be dangerous if he had to lie there for forty days or more.

He gave the same advice for travellers which we encountered in the writings of Gilbertus Anglicus and which was derived from classical times, but he had made a significant addition:

> But if the physician is in an army, then the King's tent and the tents of the physicians and surgeons should be on higher ground, facing a favourable wind: on no account should the tent be at a lower level where all the refuse gathers. Good fresh air, without any stench of corpses or any other thing, should be chosen. In summer the tent should face the south and the physician should carefully take into account everything that might bring sickness on the army and eliminate it as far as possible: such things are heat, rain, rotting corpses, diseased nuts, cabbages, trees and plants, reptiles, swamps and such like.

Gordon has a remarkable passage on the treatment of lethargy:

> And if they are in profound torpor, as I have seen many, their hair on the head, beard and chest should be pulled; they should be seized by the nose, their fingers squeezed and their lower members tightly

tied; their feet should be rubbed without mercy with salt and vinegar; sows with their young should be brought in and forced to grunt and squeak loudly, trumpets should be blown and bells rung, and drums and saws continually struck with a hammer and huge copper vessels that give out terrible sounds should be beaten; otherwise the patient will die of his torpor because he will not eat. And many die because the medical attendants think this treatment is cruel, but once the danger has been seen, the patient must not be allowed to go to sleep. I have seen many cured in this way, and I have accused the attendants of homicide because they would not allow me to try it . . . and my master died of lethargy, yet he was a choleric man, sixty years of age: a crowd of Masters were gathered together there and they agreed that a surgeon should open his veins. And he did so without any supervision from a physician. He took too much blood, and in consequence the patient became weaker and died. My own opinion is that my master became ill through too much roasted chicken given him by women: but no one can follow a decent diet when women are in charge.

For hernia Gordon advised a truss and described how it should be made.

On the whole Gordon was sound and moderate, free from argumentation and philosophising and perfectly honest about his limitations. His works were to have much influence on later English writers.

Chapter Eight

John Gaddesden

Before we deal with John Gaddesden, who reveals more than any other his indebtedness to the writers just discussed, it may be useful to mention two of Gaddesden's contemporaries, Robert de Sidesterne (*De cisterna*) and Nicholas Tyngewick. Sidesterne had probably studied at Oxford. He was ordained subdeacon 28 February 1287 and was immediately appointed rector of Newchurch, Kent, a benefice which was followed by many others in different parts of the country. He was almost certainly physician to Archbishop Pecham, whom he attended in his last illness in 1292, and by 1303 he was physician to Edward, Prince of Wales, later Edward II. He was still in the royal service in 1310.

A treatise written by him in seven books, entitled *Cure Magistri Roberti de Cisterna super Viaticum* (Sloane MS. 418), was evidently based on the works of Constantine. From the absence of the title *physicus regis* it may be inferred that the work was composed prior to 1301. It consists mainly of remedies for ailments without giving the slightest description either of the disease or its symptoms. Unlike most books of this kind it rarely quotes any author, although the names of Gariopontus, Avicenna, Rhases, Haly Abbas, Constantine and Platearius occur from time to time. The first book deals with affections of the head, vertigo, lethargy, frenzy, epilepsy, paralysis, spasmus and tremor. The second book contains all the diseases of the face, including toothache, on which, besides some curious folklore, he recommends sensible treatment. It is here that we find the source of John Gaddesden's remedy for making decayed teeth fall out, a remedy which has given rise to facetious remarks in more than one book on the history of medicine. Sidesterne says the remedy is: 'The fat of a green tree-frog applied to the tooth makes it fall out, *and therefore Avicenna says that* animals eating these frogs lose all their teeth.' Furthermore he quotes another remedy taken from Bartholomaeus Anglicus, and adds 'et ego vidi', one of the few occasions on which he records his own experience. The rest of the books are concerned with other parts of the body, proceeding, as always, from head to foot. He mentions surgery in a few cases; for instance, when a man cannot breathe because he has fractured or dislocated his spinal vertebrae 'we leave him to the surgeon'. For certain cases of hernia he recommended surgery, but also added that a leaden plate, made like a belt and attached to the body, that is, a truss, is perhaps better. It is interesting to note that when he speaks of small-pox he gives the following advice: 'or let him be wrapped up in scarlet cloth and so go to sleep.' As he makes no reference to the King's son having been cured in this way, it indicates that this remark was made before that incident took place. On scrofula he records the ordinary measures taken by physicians of the day, but does not mention that it was called 'the King's evil' or that the King of England touched for it.

On the whole it is a work without any intrinsic interest or merit and would hardly claim any attention at all were it not that it anticipates some of Gaddesden's ideas, and was the work of a man later to be considered as fit to care for the King's health.

Tyngewick was already Master of Arts by 1292, when he was inducted as rector of Broughton-Craven, Yorkshire, on the presentation of the Prior and convent of Bolton. In 1294 he was granted licence to study at a university, here or abroad, for three years, and again for three years in 1305. It was probably during this period that he gave his attention to medicine, because immediately afterwards he applied to study theology or canon law at Oxford. By 1306 he had been appointed physician to Edward I, and the following year, when he was attending the King at Carlisle, he ordered a long list of medicaments, consisting mainly of turpentine, aromatic flowers for baths, carminatives, electuaries, plasters and ointments.

How long he remained in the royal service is not known, but that he continued to practise medicine in spite of his many ecclesiastical preferments is shown by the fact that he attended Henry Eastry, Prior of Christchurch, Canterbury, and cured him of a fever after two doses of physic. He made much money by his practice and was able to give to Oxford University Beef Hall and Tyngewick Hall and provide two Masters of Arts, regents in logic, to superintend the grammar schools there. The only writing he produced was a *Tabula afforismorum* which is now among the books of Merton College.

The few facts which can be certified about John of Gaddesden show that he was a fellow of Merton College, Oxford, from 1305 to 1307. From that date until 1316 when he was appointed rector of St Nicholas, Abingdon, we hear nothing about his activities. Though some writers credit him with the degree of Bachelor of Theology, and some even with the doctorate, no documentary evidence supports it. In the papal letters he is styled simply as Master of Arts and Medicine. After holding his benefice at Abingdon for five years he applied for licence to study at an English University, and when this period expired, he applied twice more for leave of absence. That he was not residing in a college is proved by his request for Mass to be said in his lodging in 1323. He was still in Oxford in 1328 and even in 1332. As he appears as Doctor of Medicine in 1332, it would seem that his long absences from his benefices had been spent in studying medicine. In 1334 his name occurs in the accounts of Abingdon abbey as acting physician to the community, but beyond that there are no further records of his medical activity. What little we know of his practice is to be found in his own book *Rosa Anglica* where he recalls with exasperating vagueness about times and places, the various cures which he effected both on himself and on others. Apart from his famous cure of the King's son of small-pox, most of his practice was concerned with the clergy, students of philosophy, bachelors of theology, canons and so on. Rarely does he mention layfolk, though there is a reference to a woman who injured herself whilst sewing, to knights hurt at tournaments and to barber-surgeons who bought his secret remedies. He is said to have attended Joan, second daughter of

Edward III in 1341 and to have been given in 1346 a golden rose by Edward, the Black Prince, as a New Year's gift. But these details tell us little about his work.

His book, according to the prologue, was written in the seventh year of his lectureship. The generally accepted date for the composition of this work is between 1314 and 1317, the supposition being that he began to study medicine almost immediately after taking his Master of Arts degree. Apart from other considerations, this does not take into account the large borrowings made by Gaddesden from the writings of Henri de Mondeville, who did not complete his book until 1316. Furthermore Guy de Chauliac, writing in 1363 and criticising his predecessors, says that *ultimo,* last of all, there came to his hands the book of Gaddesden. It seems difficult to believe that it took almost fifty years for it to come to his notice.

Did Gaddesden study abroad between 1307 and 1316? Malgaigne has stated that Gaddesden was at Montpellier, and there are one or two details which seem to support this claim. When speaking of the frogs that make teeth fall out, he says 'and in Provence this kind of frog is found in abundance'. In another place he mentions the different wines suitable for patients, discarding those from Auxerre and Montpellier. And at another juncture, when discussing kinds of cabbage, he distinguishes them into two kinds, one from England, the other from Paris. But all these remarks are taken from other authors, Avicenna and Mondeville, so the evidence for Gaddesden's presence at Montpellier falls to the ground.

Gaddesden has been treated by most writers as a kind of untrained, uncritical, superstitious practitioner, who delighted in employing old-wives' remedies. This has been prompted partly by Guy de Chauliac's criticism, partly by the desire of medical historians to select from his work those passages which appear amusing or faintly ridiculous. A fair examination of his work does not bear out this judgement, and his early editors certainly did not share the disdain shown by the moderns.

In the first place, the book is a self-confessed compilation drawn from many authors, all of whom have a good reputation among historians of medicine: Haly Abbas, Albucasis, Avicenna, Averroes, Gilbertus Anglicus, Richardus Anglicus, Mesue, Gilles de Corbeil, John de St Amand, Theodoric of Cervia, Bernard de Gordon and Henri de Mondeville. A compilation cannot be worse than the sources from which it is taken: a coin does not lose value when it is lent or borrowed. Secondly, apart from the empirical remedies, most of which are included for the sake of completeness rather than because Gaddesden believes in their efficacy, the work is full of common sense. It is written in a most orderly manner: first it gives the description of the disease, then its causes, next its prognostic and finally its cure. In many places there are evidences of his scholastic training, but for the most part it is written well, succinctly and clearly. It is certainly an advance on the work of Gilbertus Anglicus, who is almost universally admired. He always states his own observations on cases and gives his opinion, often taking views contrary to those held by other authorities. When making quotations particularly from Avicenna he gives the exact source, so that it is always possible to verify his statements, a practice very different from that of some of his predecessors and contemporaries, who are satisfied with vague references, such as *Avicenna says*. In one instance, when dealing with leprosy, he even compares two different readings of the text of Avicenna to discover what the true meaning of the passage is. This shows sound critical sense and reveals an attitude far removed from that of the credulous and superstitious writer he is supposed to be. He even criticizes Walter Agilon and Gerard of Cremona for not having examined the text of Avicenna with care.

As examples of his common sense we may cite first his advice against too much phlebotomy, which he considers to be far more weakening than any other form of medical purgation. Taking into account the almost universal recourse to this remedy on every possible occasion and for almost every kind of ailment (including headache and toothache) it shows independence of judgement and a disinclination to be swayed either by authority or tradition. He also advised doctors against prescribing for an ailment when they had not taken into account the particular temperament or weakness of a patient: 'The physician ought carefully to enquire whether the patient is inclined to any particular form of illness besides the one which he has diagnosed and whether he usually shows any other symptoms apart from those which are manifest.' And he gives an example:

I saw a man (suffering from tinnitus) to whom the physician had given a sneezing powder made of pepper and ginger (not knowing that the patient suffered from nose-bleeding), and when he had taken it he lost so much blood that he swooned and bled for three days, so that he was thought to be dead.

He also gives very sensible advice on the care of the teeth and prescribes dentifrices 'which I have always used for my own teeth'. And for getting rid of lice, for which extraordinary remedies were often recommended, Gaddesden advises what is now common practice: 'Let the clothes be changed frequently, and the whole body be bathed or washed in salt or sulphurous water: these clean the pores in which lice are bred.'

A great deal of what Gaddesden says has been taken almost verbally from two of his contemporaries, Bernard Gordon and Henri de Mondeville, so that some of the passages in which he is thought to have recorded his own experience are nothing more than the personal recollections of his two authorities. For instance, when he is discussing dropsy and debating whether it is curable or not and stating that his procedure is to demand a fee before attempting a cure, it is Mondeville and not Gaddesden speaking. When he criticizes modern practitioners for following the teaching of Lanfranc, Roland and Bruno Longoburgo, 'whose ideas are quite wrong, as I myself have seen', he is transferring the whole passage, and much else from Mondeville again. Again: 'I myself do not like these potions, but I use wine and lint, for they belong to the old tradition of surgery and are harmful to the stomach: but I record them here so that the physician will not be ignorant of them.' This and the following page all come from Mondeville. His description of a case of stone cured by scarabs and grasshoppers, the method of examining for stone and much else, is not Gaddesden's, but Bernard Gordon's. Indeed, even the famous cure for small-pox and the reference to the King of England touching for scrofula is a little suspect when one considers that both these things had been mentioned by Sidesterne, Mondeville and Gordon before him.

But there are undoubtedly many instances of his personal experience and all the references to sickness and cures in monks must be accepted at their face value, for, as we have seen, he was attached as medical practitioner to the abbey of Abingdon. When speaking of epilepsy he remarks that the paroxysms may be apparent or hidden, sometimes long, at other times short, 'as I have seen'. As an example of this, he says: 'Sometimes the paroxysm comes on during a meal at midday or evening, as I know from a monk, but it was so short that he took no notice of it, and those near him were not aware of it, or at least only rarely.' When Gaddesden says that he cured a canon suffering from gout in the hip, or an old man 'who had gout in his hands and feet so that he could not bear anyone to touch him, and could neither get up on his feet or move', we may be certain that he is telling the truth. The same may be said for many other personal reminiscences which reflect his practice both in and around Oxford.

It has been said that, though Gaddesden wrote on surgery, he never operated himself. This statement is probably instigated by the belief that physicians never undertook any surgical treatment. In Gaddesden's case, this was not so. He gives us a definite instance when he reduced a dislocation of the jaw in one of the servants of his household. Though the description he gives of the method used is probably taken from William de Congenis, it does not invalidate the fact that he himself carried out the operation. He also carried out an operation for ranula on his father:

> I saw a small stone in my father's mouth beneath his tongue about half the size of the little finger fastened to the lower part of his palate. I excised it with a small knife and completed the cure with gargles and lotions. I have shown this stone to my students and I still carry it about with me.

He does not appear, however, to have carried out any major operation and those that he describes for dropsy, stone and hernia are probably written down at second hand. He had evidently been present at some of these operations, for the details are so clear that, unless some literary source for them can be found, it is difficult to see how otherwise he could have acquired his knowledge. His instructions for couching cataract are in this category. He defines exactly when the cataract is mature enough for the operation :

> Many surgeons are deceived, as I have often observed, because they think this ailment is something else. But if the physician or surgeon knows how to cure it, he will obtain high fees, for it is a common ailment. And I have seen men doing wonders with a needle, so that they were held in high esteem and received more money for one cure of cataract than for ten other diseases.

But it is a dangerous operation and no one should attempt it without due knowledge and experience. He suggests that the surgeon should practise first on a dog, or hen or other animal. When the operation is carried out on a person,

> the patient should sit in front of the physician in a well-lighted place whilst the sun is shining and there is no shadow. His knees should be drawn up to his chest, and bound together, so that he is almost lying down. Then he should look at the end of his nose, opening the eye that is affected: meanwhile the assistant should hold his head, bent back slightly and lift up the eye-lid. Then take the instrument or a steel needle with a round, sharp head, and begin to pierce from the side of lachrymal gland in the conjunctiva pressing it towards the pupil, beginning from the corner of the eye, and let him pierce until he comes to the covering and the pupil between the two tunicles, penetrating to the empty space of the eye which is in front of the pupil. And let the surgeon hold the eye until the perforation is complete, and press the needle down until it is hidden beneath the cornea. . . .

His description of the hernia operation is probably taken from Bernard Gordon, for when he advises a truss instead of the operation, which is frequently fatal, his description of the truss comes from the same source. On the cure of ulcers, cancers and fistulae, Gaddesden follows Mondeville, sometimes copying him verbatim, sometimes drastically abridging his text; but he adds: 'Note that *fistulae ani* ought not to be cured, but to be treated with palliatives, just like haemorrhoids, lest after the cure there arise involuntary release of the faeces', a significant comment on the result of some of these operations. On the whole, then, Gaddesden should not be dismissed as a mere empiric, a purveyor of charms and folk-lorish remedies. There are examples of these things in his work, but the rational, fundamentally sound practice contained in his lengthy compilation far outweighs these few and disparate elements. His wide reading and his long experience had made him tolerant of different and widely opposite notions and, except where positive harm and injury would ensue, he accepted these notions as possible in the exercise of an art which was not based on mathematical certainty. He was willing to learn from any source, whether country crones or royal physicians and surgeons, and it is this characteristic which makes his work so readable and instructive. Indeed, Gaddesden had this purpose in mind, for, when he says at the beginning of the book, 'As the rose is pre-eminent among all flowers, so this book excels all other practical manuals of medicine', he was not, as some think, showing overweening conceit, but stating what he considered to be a fact. For he adds: 'it has been written both for rich and poor, for surgeons as well as physicians.' Up till then no book on medicine had catered for so wide an audience, but had been addressed to a limited and specific group of people. In the *Rosa Anglica* there was something for everyone, for the professional and the amateur, for the academic and the country practitioner, for those who could afford expensive remedies and those who had to fend for themselves. And all of it could claim some kind of authority or tradition.

In Gaddesden, then, we see for the first time in England a synthesis of all that appeared on the continent during the previous two centuries: the translations from Arabic writers, the writings of the Salernitans, the fruit of progressive work in surgery from Italy and the final word (at that time) from the two most recent products of Montpellier and Paris. It was no small achievement for a man who, presumably, had never set foot outside England; and though his compilation may have its defects, it does not suffer from incompleteness.

Chapter Nine

Anatomy

One of the bitterest critics of Gaddesden was Guy de Chauliac, surgeon to the Popes at Avignon and a friend of Petrarch. He had an exalted idea of his own position and showed the greatest contempt for practically all his contemporaries and forbears, with the exception of Galen. 'They follow each other like geese', he said; and of his own work, written towards the end of his life to lessen the tedium of old age: 'I hope it will be useful, though it will be wasted on some, almost as if one were talking to donkeys.' He opens his book with an historical account of the development of medicine and surgery up to his day, an account which all writers on the history of medicine have considered to be the first since Celsus described what had passed before his time. But in fact this 'singular chapter' is nothing but a rehash and abridgement of what Henri de Mondeville had written some fifty years earlier. It is typical of Chauliac that he nowhere acknowledges help or information from anyone, though a close examination of his work proves it to be as derivative and as much a compilation as the works he derides. He had read widely, studying first at Montpellier, then at Bologna under Bertuccio, from whom he learned anatomy; but in spite of his many contributions to surgery, he was, in general, a reactionary. This prevented him from following Henri de Mondeville and Theodoric in their simple method of treating wounds; and his persistence in employing cautery, salves and plasters retarded the progress of surgery for centuries.

The wide diffusion of his work, however, had one great merit. It drew attention to the fundamental importance of a knowledge of anatomy:

The knowledge of anatomy is acquired in two ways; one is by books, but though this is useful, it is insufficient to impart all that can be learned by observation . . . the second way is by dissecting dead bodies, namely, of those who have been recently beheaded or hanged. By this means we learn the anatomy of the internal organs, the muscles, skin, veins and sinews, especially regarding their origin. Mondino of Bologna, who wrote about this, made dissections many times, and my master Bertuccio followed the same procedure, placing the dead body on a table and dealing with it in four lectures. In the first he used to deal with the nutritive members because they putrefy first; in the second, he dealt with the spiritual members; in the third, with the animated and lastly with the extremities. . . . We dissect bodies that have been dried in the sun, or corrupted in the earth, or washed in running water, or boiled: and from this we discover the anatomy of the bones, cartilages, joints, large sinews, and muscles. And we can learn anatomy in this way from the bodies of men, asses, pigs and many other animals, and even through illustrations, such as Henri de Mondeville made for instruction in anatomy.

Mondino di Luzzi, who taught Chauliac's master, Bertuccio, had taught at Bologna from 1290 to 1326. He is known to have made autopsies on two women in 1315, but these were by no means the only occasions on which he had carried out dissections. When speaking of the umbilicus he says: 'This is more noticeable in unborn babies than in the born, *as I have shown many times*', a clear reference to dissection of women who had died before childbirth. But, as Chauliac had also mentioned, dissection of animals, particularly of pigs, continued, and the old Salernitan method of washing away the flesh from a corpse in running water the better to show the bones was also continued. Mondino's book, however, was the first book on anatomy in the Middle Ages which had dissection of the human corpse as its basis. That is why it eclipsed all its predecessors, the *Anatomia porci* attributed to Copho and the other Salernitan treatises, the fourth book of William of Saliceto and the work of Mondeville. It had one serious defect: though the anatomy was good, the reasoning was not. Mondino depended too much for his account of the functions of various parts of the body on older writers and even when he had the facts under his eyes, he could not dissociate himself from the pronouncements of his authorities. So he still spoke of the heart having three ventricles, of the heart generating spirit from the blood by heat and evaporation, of the five lobes of the liver and so on. Though his was the work of a pioneer, his book appears to have by-passed the physicians completely and nowhere was accepted as a text to be included in the University curriculum.

How then were surgeons taught their craft? It has always been assumed that it was merely a question of apprenticeship, that a practising surgeon took into his employ one or two assistants and that they learned the profession by watching, helping the master in small ways and eventually performing operations themselves. This is, to a certain extent, true. But as we have seen from Willam de Congenis, from Lanfranc and Henri de Mondeville, surgeons had their own school to which students from the Universities and even Regent Masters came for instruction. These would be men already well versed in medicine, so that quite a number of surgeons were not merely craftsmen, not merely 'manual operators' as the physicians superciliously termed them, but men of high professional standard in both branches of medicine. This was particularly true of Italy, but it was also true of France, as the example of Guy de Chauliac proves. The physicians, however, holding (as they did) the key positions in the Universities, were the ruling body when it was a question of granting permission to practise either medicine or surgery, and this clearly emerges at the beginning of the fourteenth century in the statutes laid down by the city of Venice. Already in 1281 it had been decreed that no surgeon should exercise his profession before he had taken an oath before the Justices, and the same obligations to report all wounding, cases of homicide, and poisoning, which we have already seen in the contract signed earlier in the century by Hugh of Lucca, were imposed upon them. Later on, in 1321, these decrees were perfected, so that all doctors inscribed on the rolls of the College, whether physicians or surgeons, were bound to give their views on cases of wounding, and in this way formed a body of medical and legal experts in the service of the Republic. In this same year it was laid down that:

if any surgeon (*medicus Chirurgiae*) wished to practise, he could not do so until he had been first examined or taken his doctorate in the University (*studio generali*). If he had not taken a degree, then the head of the surgeons' faculty, together with his counsellors, was to examine him. But the head of the surgeons' faculty was to have with him the head of the medical faculty (*priorem medicorum phisicae*) and his counsellors at the examination, and if the candidate was found competent by them all, he could practise in Venice and become a member of the College.

This clearly shows that the physicians still held the deciding vote in the admission of surgeons and that what they were demanding was a knowledge of medicine. Nothing could be more illuminating on this point than the decree of the Great Council made on 23 June, 1328. On that day they decided that 'Master Mondino, doctor of physic of Bologna, recommended as being most competent in the science of medicine and in other sciences', of which they had testimonials from all who knew him, should be taken into the service of the Republic at a stipend of ten lire a year 'on condition that he passes the examination'. This shows both the extraordinary standard set by the Council of Venice and the jealously guarded 'gild' formed by the physicians. By that date Mondino had been a doctor for thirty-two years, had lectured and written on anatomy almost as long and had attained a European reputation, both for his practice and his many commentaries on the *De juvamentis* of Galen and the texts in the *Articella*. On the other hand we find the Great Council absolving a certain master Domenico, *once a cobbler*, but now instructed in the art of surgery, from a fine for having abused the art in past times. This man was expert in fractures and had many outstanding cures to his credit, and in spite of the fact that he could not read, had not been considered suitable by the Examiners, nor inscribed as a member of the College, was still allowed to practise. This recalls Guy de Chauliac's remark when laying down the qualities required in a surgeon, namely, that he be literate, expert in practice, inventive and of good character, 'otherwise the cobblers, carpenters, smiths and others will promptly lay aside their crafts and take up the practice of medicine'.

Whereas instruction in surgery at Bologna was sufficiently

advanced and practical to induce Italian and foreign surgeons, like Chauliac, to go there for the improvement of their technical knowledge, it is extremely doubtful whether any student would have proceeded to the Universities of Oxford or Cambridge for the purpose of qualifying as a surgeon. At the English universities practical instruction in surgery seems to have been ignored, but this does not necessarily mean that training was not available in the university cities themselves. As we have seen from the remarks of Gaddesden, he held schools for training surgeons, though these may have been in a private capacity. The surgeons who existed at Oxford and Cambridge were mainly, if not entirely, local practitioners: some of them were undoubtedly men who had studied medicine at the University, but they could not impart their knowledge of surgery within the University framework and must have held classes for those of the medical students who required tuition in halls or lodgings of their own. The surgeons could secure from the Chancellor a licence to practise in the municipality, but they could not obtain a degree. This does not mean, as some think, that they ranked little, if at all, above the apothecaries and spicers who sold roots and balsam in the High Street. Most of them were highly literate people and the evidence that we possess proves that they could not only read, but write in English, Latin and French. We must beware of subscribing to Sir Clifford Allbutt's strictures: 'Surgeons, reared in base apprenticeships, not only illiterate, but forbidden even the name of learning, lay under heavy disadvantages.' If this were so, why did Gaddesden, writing in Latin, address his book not merely to physicians, but to surgeons also?

Outside academic circles young surgeon apprentices would be entirely dependent for training upon their masters, craftsmen tied by their business to certain localities and limited in their access to new and improved methods of treatment. For his professional qualifications the barber surgeon apprentice depended largely upon his industry, his manual skill, his business acumen and the benevolence of his employer in sponsoring his candidature for admission to membership of a gild. But this in no sense implies that he was deficient in formal education or that he had no access to treatises on surgery. One of the outstanding English surgeons of this

I *Scorpion and snake fighting; the plant is 'Solago Minor' which, it is thought, corresponds to the* Heliotropium Europaeum *of botanists. From* Cotton Vitellius C. III. fo. 40, *an Anglo-Saxon work of about* 1050

daci minstice districte nenenu.

Ad pe°sii ferro l' siide q̃ se iuiar pationir. Herba Arginii cũ Aceto iposita psothissime

Nomen herbe. Cyclaminos. Omoeos. Ceseron. Alii. Annon. Alii. Cassosillos. Alii. Chedomion. Zoro astes. Chaehena. Alii. Sampaues. dicunt. Alii. Bostanes.

II Top *Physicians offer draughts of Agrimony to two warriors to cure sword wounds.* Bottom *Physician offers a draught of Cyclamine against serpent bite: the herb is shown at the side of the picture. From Brit. Mus. Harl. MS. 5294*

III 13th-century Gynaecology: Top *A bowl of water is placed on the breast of a female patient to see if she has died or merely fainted.* Bottom *Giving an inhalant to a swooning woman. From* MS. Ashmole 399 *in the Bodleian Library*

Sim prolib. descendit aliqua parte
matris. reliquum corp? inchituerit.
qui facere delemus. sicut diximus su
perius. obstetrix i missa manu cum
componat. z deinde adducat.

Si diuisis pedibus duabus parti
bus uulue. plantas intingat quid
faciemus. inmissa manu obstetrix
eos uingat. z ad orificium matricis
eos componat. z sic adducat.

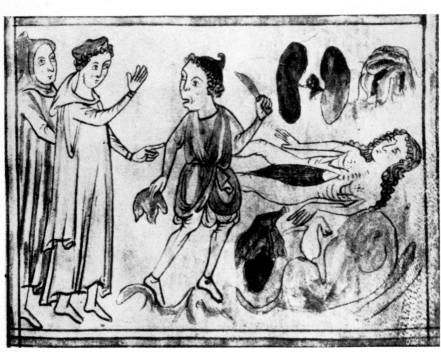

IV Top 13th-century Obstetrics: various foetal positions. From Soranus of Ephesus MS. Ashmole 399 fo. 34r. Bottom A dissection scene, c. 1298. From MS. Ashmole 399

v *Illuminated manuscript* Practica Rogerii, *the lower six drawings dealing with luxation. From the* 13th-century Brit. Mus. Sloane MS. 1977

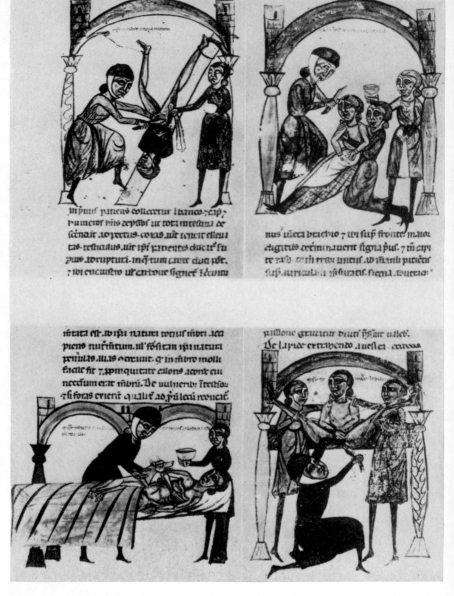

VI *Miniature showing various operations including one for rupture, an operation on the head, an abdominal operation and cutting for stone. From* Roland's Surgery. *Bibl.* Casanatense Codex 1382

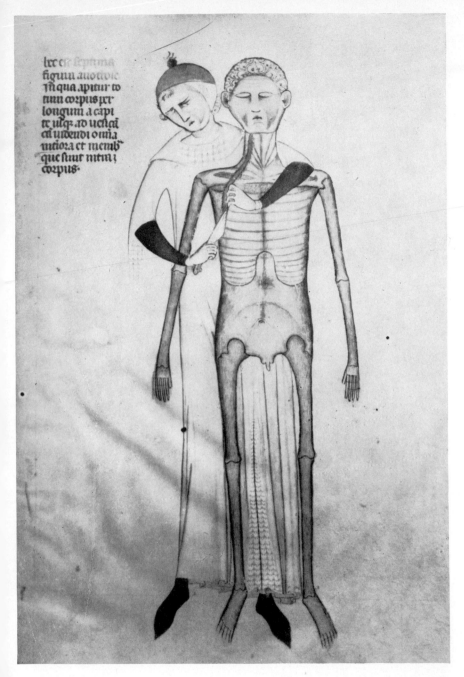

VII *An anatomical plate showing the incision to be made for revealing the internal organs.* From Guido de Vigevano MS. 334 (569) *in Musée Condé, Chantilly*

period, and a younger contemporary of Gaddesden, is confirmation of it.

John Arderne (1307–92) is supposed to have been a member of the distinguished Warwickshire family of Ardernes, but it is unlikely that a man from such a background, with sheriffs and justiciars for relatives, should have taken up a craft of this kind. Nothing is known of his early life, but his works reveal that though he had not attended a university, he had received a liberal education: he always refers to himself as *chirurgus inter medicos*, that is, not a medical man with a degree, but a surgeon pure and simple. Yet his grasp of all the medical literature then available is complete: he quotes nearly all the previous writers on surgery, Roger, Roland, Lanfranc, Jamerius, and probably Guy de Chauliac; he borrows from Gilbertus Anglicus, Roger de Baron, John of St Amand, Walter Agilon, Gilles de Corbeil, Theophilus; he knows the Arabs Johannitius, Isaac Judaeus, Avicenna, Serapion, and the works of Hippocrates and Galen on whom these writers had commented. Indeed, his reading is as wide as that of Gaddesden and equal in value to that demanded by academic standards.

But Arderne had been trained in a school that no amount of University lecturing could compare with, that profitable school of surgical experience, the battlefield. He had been in the train of Henry Plantagenet, Duke of Lancaster, and afterwards of John of Gaunt, King of Castille and Leon. He had first followed the Duke to Flanders about 1338, then to Spain in 1343, and finally to Aquitaine about 1345. Though Arderne does not say specifically that he had served the Duke in the latter campaign, it is obvious from his intimate knowledge of the towns which were invaded by the army, Gascony, Bordeaux, Bergerac, Toulouse, Narbonne and Poitiers (named not in their geographical order but in the order they were invaded), that he was present. When the campaign was ended, 1347 to 1348, he returned to London, bought himself a small estate at Mitcham, Surrey, and after the death of his wife during the plague, he retired to Newark in Nottinghamshire, where he stayed until 1370.

In his old age he set himself to write a system of surgery, consisting of a series of separate treatises dealing with specific subjects, which were afterwards collected into one volume entitled *Practica Magistri Joannis de Arderne,* though various combinations of the treatises were also arranged. The first section of his book deals with haemorrhage: it gives instructions on the occasions when a patient should be bled, and how to stop bleeding in cancer, piles and menorrhagia. Other sections deal with diseases of the eyes, diseases of the male generative organs, diseases of women, diseases of the kidneys, intestinal obstruction, gout and fistulae. The manuscripts containing this material are abundantly illustrated and not only are the various diseases vividly depicted (often with the patients, priests, canon, monks, noblemen shown suffering from these ills), but the manner of treating them, with the instruments employed and the different stages in the operation, are also shown. This makes the book extremely readable, for it not only presents a picture of the practice and the problems of the surgeon, but also the conditions under which patients lived in the fourteenth century. Often he fills his pages with his personal reminiscences, giving names and dates of his patients with exact descriptions of their diseases and their symptoms; but when he is recalling cases which involved noblemen he merely draws their coat of arms in the margin, a sign of great discretion and tact. Often his egotistical remarks reveal his disdain for other practitioners, but on the whole he observes the advice he had given to others, not speaking ill when he can speak well.

In practice he appears to have based his success on careful preparation and planning. When operating he was bold, though careful to avoid irritants and pus-forming salves, and always insisting on cleanliness. His exact clinical observations and his careful recording of case notes, show how gradually he built up his enormous experience which gave him great confidence when he was faced with complicated surgical operations. In spite of this and his complete command of surgical technique, he could not rid himself of reliance on astrology, and even when he undertook the operation for *fistula in ano,* which he had invented, he was always careful to choose a day on which the influence of the moon would not be baneful. Neither was he averse to the use of charms, though it may be that late compilers of his work have placed more emphasis on this aspect of his book than he did himself.

The numerous copies of his works which survive testify to their popularity, the most successful of all being his treatise *De fistula in ano*, dealing with a surgical operation which had always been considered up to that time to be impossible. It was on this operation that he lays his claim to fame and it was by this, as he confesses, that he acquired a considerable fortune.

What is surprising in a man of such wide knowledge is that he appears to have been unaware of the great strides made abroad in the study of anatomy. Nowhere in his treatises is there any explicit teaching on this subject nor does he seem to have considered that a knowledge of anatomy was essential for the perfect practice of surgery. This is an indication of the backwardness in some respects of medical education in this country. On the other hand, it would have been perfectly easy for Arderne to have copied into his books those parts of Lanfranc and Mondeville which deal with this question; and his omission of them may indicate that he was more concerned in giving practical instruction, based on his personal experience, than in handing on mere theory which he took for granted.

It is said that about 1370 Arderne came to London and joined the gild of Barber-surgeons: a number of references in official records to a John de Arderne may refer to him, but there is no certainty on this score. But if Arderne was a member of the gild, he may have joined as a result of the law enacted in 1363 that every man must join some kind of gild, and if no gild existed for his particular craft, then he must join some other. Thus it was that the Barbers' gild had in its ranks physicians, surgeons, apothecaries, silk weavers, chandlers and rope-makers. The object of the gilds was to exercise a kind of monopoly over the practice of their craft, to regulate conditions of work, to set ethical standards of their profession and to guard the privileges of their members. The fellowship of the Fraternity of Surgeons had existed long before 1369, whilst the Fraternity of Barbers was mentioned in records as early as 1308. Between these two crafts there had been a struggle to obtain the power of supervision, and we find that whereas in 1369 and in 1380 the surgeons had this power, the barbers won back the right in 1376 and again in 1415. The practice of surgery therefore was in some measure supervised and controlled, whilst among the physicians no such control existed.

In 1388 Richard II, by the authority of a Parliament held at Cambridge, issued a writ demanding that Masters and Wardens of all gilds and fraternities should submit to the royal Chancery a return describing the foundation of their gilds and the method employed in governing them. They had to reveal the oath taken when entering the fraternity, particulars of their meetings, customs and privileges, lists of properties and copies of charters or letters patent, if such existed. The information produced by the Barbers of the City tell us little about their work, and the details they mention chiefly concern the mutual responsibility to support members in poverty, religious observances, disputes about business, payment of dues, encroachments on each other's households and practice, and so on. We have to wait until the next century before any real knowledge about their professional responsibilities and activities becomes available.

Chapter Ten

The Ordinary Medieval Practitioner

The recitation of the deeds and writings of the more celebrated medical men who lived during the twelfth, thirteenth and fourteenth centuries affords us very little insight into the actual practice of their less favoured and less known contemporaries. Whilst we know a great deal about the physicians and surgeons who worked in the courts of Popes and Kings and about some of those who taught in the universities, our knowledge of the ordinary medical man who was limited to small towns and to the service of a humbler clientele is meagre. His name will appear in official documents only when he is guilty of some misdemeanour, when he falls into debt or claims his fees, when he has a quarrel with his neighbour or is rewarded for his faithful services by a grateful patron. Apart from occasions like this his medical practice received no recognition and his working life was shrouded in obscurity.

Fortunately, one or two manuscripts survive which not only provide some evidence of the competence, standard of education, methods of practice and principles of the ordinary medical practitioner, but also indicate the relative stagnation of the medical profession as a whole. These manuscripts are not like the books one would ordinarily find in a monastic or private library; they are not commonplace books or records of cases. They are tables of various kinds, containing a calendar, canons of the eclipses of the sun, canons of the eclipses of the moon, tables of planets, rules for phlebotomy and an analysis of urines. With all these available, the physician could make rapid calculations and decide within a matter of seconds what was ailing the patient, what the treatment should be and what success or failure was likely to ensue. These manuscripts consisted of seven or eight pieces of parchment, folded across the middle and then folded again into three sections, so that the outward appearance showed only narrow strips each measuring about seven inches long and two inches wide. Each one of these strips was devoted to one aspect of a diagnosis, the actual date when illness began, the position of the sun and moon during its continuance, the planet governing the part of the body affected, the actual vein which must be cut and the twenty-four kinds of urine with their significance. Some of these manuscripts had additional elements, such as the Sphere of Apuleius, by which the medical practitioner through taking the patient's name, giving a numeral quantity to each letter and subtracting thirty from it, could discover whether the person would live or die. Some even had a table for calculating what would happen in the future, so that it became possible not only to foretell the weather, but also to find stolen property and lay hands on the thief. These ready-reckoners, as one might term them, hung from a belt or girdle round the waist and had their counterpart in the manuscripts of the same form which were worn by monks and friars and which contained tables of virtues and vices, scriptural examples, points for sermons or copies of the psalms.

Besides the tables mentioned above, the manuscripts contained illustrations showing the various phases in the eclipses both of sun and moon, the zodiac man, the venous man and a roundel of urinals with the exact colours ranging from lemon to red. The repetition of these illustrations (not always of the same artistic standard) accompanied by the same texts points to a steady trade and output in the kind of manuscript we are describing and it is probable, judging by the calendars and the tables of eclipses, that they were produced in large numbers by the stationers of Oxford, who had carried on a flourishing book trade from the twelfth century onwards. The coloured illustrations were accompanied with captions which gave, in even briefer form, the instructions contained in the texts and enabled the medical practitioner to decide at a glance where on the body phlebotomy was to be carried out and what significance could be attached to the urine.

The importance accorded to astrology, as evidenced by its holding first place in the manuscript, need not astonish the reader. Viewed against the background of popular medicine, of charmed potions, amulets, magical incantations and the like, this astrological medicine presented an aspect of precise and co-ordinated knowledge based on an accurate, determined and predictable order of the heavens. It was 'scientific' in the sense that it was based on principles elaborated during classical times and handed down almost unchanged in the later centuries. These principles laid down that man was a microcosm composed, like the macrocosm of which he was part, of four primary elements (earth, air, fire, and water), with four qualities (heat, cold, moistness, and dryness). His characteristic nature and individual temperament (sanguine, choleric, phlegmatic, or melancholic) arose from the predominance in his make-up of one of these four constituent and vital fluids. Indeed, his entire physical constitution corresponded to a sympathetic relationship between himself and the celestial spheres, the zodiac (or exterior belt) governing his outward anatomy, the planets (or inner circles) dominating his inner organs. Of all the planets, the moon, which was closest to the centre of this anthropocentric scheme, exercised the greatest influence on terrestrial fluids (that is the tides) and consequently was the cause of the increase or decrease in man of the humoral fluids. The pathology, which issued from these general principles, regarded illness primarily in terms of the disturbance of man's humoral balance. One method of correcting this disturbance of the humours was phlebotomy. This naturally took pride of place in medical treatment, and as a result tables of reference indicating where blood was to be taken from, what the age or strength of the patient should be, at what season of the year it should be practised and under what astrological signs it should be avoided, were incorporated into the physician's books as a practical necessity. Since the physician could not be expected to hold in his memory the changing phases of the moon, signs and planets, and as, without them, strictly correct treatment was deemed to be impossible, he had to depend on these complex calendrical tables, reduced to as simple a form as possible. When the system reached its highest perfection during the late fourteenth and early fifteenth centuries, exact calculations by precision instruments, similar to those of the astronomers and navigators, were employed, and many of these physicians' manuscripts contain a volvella with adjustable parts to enable him to work out these calculations with extraordinary accuracy. This complex system was applied not merely to bloodletting, but also to general medicine and hygiene, particularly as regards purging, bathing, medication, and surgery. But since more danger was incurred in bloodletting, not merely because the patient might be weakened too much or even bleed to death, but also because the incision might not heal and cause other complications, greater importance was attached to it. It became the subject of civic and national concern and eventually statutes were enacted requiring every doctor to consult such tables before cutting a vein.

The same danger was not incurred in the prognostication from urine and consequently this was the commonest form of diagnosis. It had been reduced to a fine art by the Arabs at a very early stage and remained unchanged for centuries, so that the urinal flask became almost the supreme symbol of the medical profession.

It will be seen, then, that within a small compass the physician possessed all the essential information he was likely to need when first called to examine a patient. By flipping his finger through the various tables he could find out very quickly what ailment the man was prone to, how serious, through the intervention of the planets, it was likely to be and what immediate advice he should give. Detailed treatment with drugs or surgery would undoubtedly follow in cases of prolonged sickness, but for a rapid diagnosis and a superficial alleviation of his symptoms, his little book would supply his present needs.

No matter how sympathetic one may be to these medieval ideas and practices, it cannot blind us to the fact that the competence and limitations of the ordinary physician in dealing with disease are blatantly exposed by the existence of such ready-reckoners.

They enable us to discover the actual treatment meted out to patients in contradistinction to the theories and ideals expressed by famous writers in their works. They throw immense light on the state of medical knowledge at the end of the Middle Ages and they show that in spite of the considerable skill and intellectual attainments of some of the giants, whose contributions to medical science are deservedly praised, the ordinary medical practitioner was bound hand and foot by ideas and theories that had remained static since classical times. The old phrases, the old doctrines, the old treatment were repeated like sentences from a child's catechism and the result of centuries of scientific and literary endeavour were reduced to a formula.

Perhaps this can best be illustrated by giving extracts from some parts of the vade-mecum. Omitting the tables of the eclipses of the sun and moon, we begin with the tables of the planets:

This table of the planets is to be used by finding the day at the top of the page and the hours at the left: where they coincide, the planet will be found which is in control at that hour, for each planet has particular influence above all others on the day and hour which is named after it . . .The table of the moon is useful for blood-letting, but as art imitates nature, each action should be done in its own time. An unstable sign is said to designate a quick change; a fixed one, stability; but a common sign, repetition and solution.

It is useful therefore to have an eye to the sign through which the moon is passing. The moveable signs are Aries, Cancer, Libra and Capricorn, with which the four seasons of the year begin, namely, Spring, Summer, Autumn and Winter, each one of which follows its own and a common sign.

To find the sign and degree of the moon quickly, begin at the top of the table with the sign and degree in which they join, or with the degree nearest to it (with the lowest number) and the age of the moon: where they meet you will find the degree; what corresponds to that sign is shown by the green lines leading transversally to it and enclosing it.

THE IMAGE OF THE SIGNS

ARIES   Avoid incisions in the head and face and cut no vein in the head.

TAURUS   Avoid incisions in the neck and throat and cut no vein there.

GEMINI   Avoid incisions in the shoulders and arms or hands and cut no vein.

CANCER   Avoid incisions in the breast and sides, lesions in the stomach and lungs, and cut no vein that goes to the spleen.

LEO   Avoid incisions of the nerves, lesions of the sides and bones, and do not cut the back either by opening or bleeding.

VIRGO   Avoid opening a wound in the belly and in internal parts.

LIBRA   Avoid opening wounds in the umbilicus and parts of the belly and do not open a vein in the back or do cupping.

SCORPIO   Avoid cutting the testicles, anus, vesica, and do not cut the verenda in man or woman.

SAGITTARIUS   Avoid incisions in the thighs and fingers and do not cut blemishes or growths.

CAPRICORN   Avoid cutting the knees or the veins and sinews in these places.

AQUARIUS   Avoid cutting the legs and any place as far as the heels.

PISCES   Avoid cutting the feet.

ON BLOOD-LETTING

Blood-letting is done by juxtaposition or by opposition. If an ailment is chronic, blood-letting is done by juxtaposition, but if of recent origin by opposition. It is said to be done by juxtaposition when the blood is drawn from the part where the sickness lies, by opposition when the blood is drawn from the opposite part. . . .

In Phlebotomy four things are to be kept in mind: time, habit, age and strength. During very hot weather phlebotomy should not be undertaken because humours are engendered then and the good humours flow out as quickly as the bad. Nor should phlebotomy be done in very cold weather, because the humours are compacted in the body and difficult to draw out, and the good come out quicker than the bad.

Phlebotomy should not be done at the new moon because the body is empty of humours at that time and by letting blood they would be completely drained out.

Habit is to be considered: even if an old man has been used to blood-letting, he should not be let blood because of his weakness.

Age must be taken into consideration, since no one should be let blood before the age of twelve nor in decrepit old age; yet some who are vigorous may be blooded. Strength should be the criterion, for the strong ought to be let blood, but the weak not at all.

A man suffering from congestion, (that is, from too much blood) or from a fever (that is, from unhealthy blood), should be cut immediately the moon passes through the middle of the sign of Gemini....

If the blood appears black, draw it off until it becomes red. If it is thick, until it thins out: if watery, until it becomes thick. If the blood cannot flow because the mouth of the wound is closed, open it with a finger and the blood will come out with a rush. ...

Phlebotomy clears the mind, strengthens the memory, cleanses the stomach, dries up the brain, warms the marrow, sharpens the hearing, stops tears, encourages discrimination, develops the senses, promotes digestion, produces a musical voice, dispels torpor, drives away anxiety, feeds the blood, rids it of poisonous matter, and brings long life. It eliminates rheumatic ailments, gets rid of pestilent diseases, cures pains, fevers and various sicknesses and makes the urine clean and clear.

If anyone is let blood incorrectly, put hot leaves of hyosciamus moistened with oil near or over the affected place. ...

A CURE FOR CUT VEINS

Rub a leaf of rue boiled in laurel oil on the arm or place where the wound is: or boil a bean in wine until it dissolves, add as much grease as is necessary, and then bind it hot on the arm in a cloth. If the cephalic vein swells, treat it with water and oil, warm in summer, cold in winter, putting diaquilon on it. If the median vein swells, plaster it with a leaf of beet in a bandage which has been steeped in oil of roses.

If you let blood on the 11th April or 17th March
You will not suffer blindness.
If you submit to blood-letting on the 4th or 5th of May
You will never be taken by fever.
In March and May blood should be taken from the right,
In Autumn from the left....
The days best for blood-letting are the feastday of St Valentine in February and the feastday of St Lambert in September.

RULES ABOUT URINE

Urine that is ruddy betokens health and the good estate of the body: urine that is slightly ruddy shows good health, but not as perfect as that of ruddy urine.

Red urine, or rose colour, signifies ephemeral fever: and if the patient frequently makes water, it signifies continuous fever.

Urine red like blood is a sign of fever caused by too much blood: blood should be let immediately when the moon is passing through the sign of Gemini. Green urine, coming after red, is a sign of inflammation, a mortal sickness.

Red urine which is muddy shows that the sickness is nearing its end.

Red urine mixed with mucous signifies heating of the liver.

Pale urine shows a weakness of the stomach and a delayed second digestion.

In a healthy man urine like well-water shows crude humours, but in acute fevers it is a sign of death.

A milky urine of rather thick substance is not as dangerous in women as it is in men; it arises from an unhealthy matrix, but in acute fevers is a sign of death.

Urine which is milky on the surface, dark at the bottom and clear in the middle is a sign of dropsy. But ruddy urine in a dropsical patient is a sign of death. . . .

Saffron-coloured urine with thick, smelly, and frothy substance is a sign of jaundice. . . .

Urine which is clear in the bottom half, but dense and thin at the top is a sign of congestion of the chest.

Frothy, clear and slightly red urine shows that there is greater pain on the right than on the left.

Where the urine is frothy high up, it shows there is more pain on the left, for the left side is colder than the right.

Thin and pale urine which is clear shows acidity and phlegm. If the surface of the urine trembles without anyone shaking it, it is a sign of the flow of phlegm and other humours from the head through the neck to the lower members.

Urine that is thick, reddish and milky shows that there is gout in the upper parts of the body. . . .

All urine is a filter of the blood and properly indicates two things, either an affection of the liver and veins, or an affection of the intestines and vesica. Of other things it gives only indirect indications.

In urine different points are to be considered, namely colour, place, and content. The reasons for its texture, its colour, and its sediment are different. For since there are four qualities in the human body, namely, heat, cold, dryness and moistness, these are the causes of texture and colour. Heat is the cause of a red colour, cold of white; dryness is the reason for a thin texture, moistness for a thick texture.

Urine is divided into parts: the top part is called the circle (or surface), the second part is the body of air, the third is perforation, the fourth is the bottom.

From the circle we can diagnose ailments of the head and brain, from the second part ailments of the spiritual members and the stomach.

There are three positions of the urine, bottom middle and top. The bottom begins at the lowest part of the urinal flask and extends to the breadth of two fingers: the middle position begins when the lowest part stops and extends to the circle which lies at the top: and when there is froth at the top, it indicates wind or inflation or some other ailment of the lungs.

If the circle is thick, it indicates excessive pain in the head. . . .

In the lowest position there are sometimes small, sandy particles, and then it means that the patient is suffering from stone. If the sediment is black, this is poisonous matter expelled by the urine and is a sign of death. . . .

As will readily be recognised, some of these ideas were already current in the ninth century, whilst the latter part of the text on urines is taken almost bodily from the treatise of Isaac Judaeus, made available to the West by Constantine in the eleventh century. That they should still be current in the fifteenth and form the stock-in-trade of most physicians, who had presumably spent a number of years at a university studying medicine, is a devastating comment on the lack of enterprise shown by the medical profession of those days.

Chapter Eleven

Medical Ethics
and Etiquette

The mention of gilds as having some control over the ethics of the medical profession coupled with the long passages on this matter in the writings of William de Saliceto, Lanfranc, Mondeville and Arderne, shows us that both physicians and surgeons in the Middle Ages were conscious of their status and their responsibilities both to their profession and their patients. This preoccupation with codes of behaviour, with professional qualifications and with justice towards the sick had a long history and the *De adventu medici ad aegrotum* of the Salernitan school was by no means the first treatise to deal with it. Already in the ninth century there were small tracts of this kind deriving from Hippocratic works, such as the *Decorum* and *Precepts* (which may have been translated in the fifth or sixth century) and one Paris manuscript contains no less than seven concerning the training, character and behaviour of the physician. Though most of this literature is probably based on Italian sources, it is noticeable that it all stems from trans-alpine monasteries, and it can therefore be taken to represent what has been called 'monastic medicine'.

On the character demanded from one who proposed to undertake the care of the sick we find this advice:

First, he should test his personality to see that he is of gracious and innately good character, apt and inclined to learn, sober, and modest, a good conversationalist, charming, conscientious, intelligent, vigilant and affable. . . . He should not be timid, turbulent or proud, scornful or lascivious or garrulous, a publican or a woman-lover, but rather full of counsel, learned and chaste. He should not be drunken or lewd, fraudulent, vulgar, criminal or disgraceful. . . . Inasmuch as the physician is held in high honour, he should have no faults, but rather discretion, few words, patience, quietness, and refinement; not greed, but rather restraint; he should be sensitive, reasonable, hard-working and dignified.

Regarding the physician's education they had this to say:

Whoever wishes to become proficient in the art of medicine ought to be capable of prolonged study, so that by constant reading of different books his perception and judgement reach that point where learning becomes easy . . . Before studying medicine he should be well instructed in all subjects . . . First of all he should be taught grammar, dialectic, astronomy, arithmetic, geometry and music . . . and be taught philosophy along with medicine.

This was the course prescribed by Isidore in the seventh century and which was widely diffused through his *Etymologies*.

On the question of fees it is remarked:

He should take care of the rich and poor, slave and free, quite impartially, for medicine is needed by all classes of people. If recompense is offered, he should accept rather than refuse it. But if it is not offered, it should not be demanded, because no matter how much payment is made for medical services, it can never equal the benefits conferred.

On etiquette instructions are precise:

The physician's appearance and approach should be distinguished. In his dress he should not use too much purple nor be too fastidious about cutting his hair frequently. Everything should be in moderation. . . . In his approach to the patient he should not hold up his head arrogantly nor lower his glance as if he is hesitant, but bend his head slightly.

In the physician's relations with women it says:

Enter a home without injuring or corrupting it. Beware lest your medicines bring death to anyone. Do not allow women to persuade you to give abortives, and do not be a party to any such plan, but keep yourself without blemish and undefiled. Keep yourself free from carnal relations with the maid-servants, children, married women, virgins and widows. And whatever you hear in the course of your treatment, unless it is something that ought to be reported and judged, keep secret.

These passages, chosen out of many, provide valuable evidence for the medieval ideals of training, character, qualifications, dress and deportment of physicians. Their marked resemblance to material contained in the Hippocratic works indicate a fusion of ideas taken from classical antiquity and christianity during the early centuries. They do not breathe that other-worldly spirit which the predominantly religious atmosphere of the Middle Ages is supposed to have fostered, and already at this early stage the secular outlook is in evidence. With progress of time the more materialistic element was to prevail, so that by the thirteenth and fourteenth centuries, though some of the ideals expressed here were to survive, the emphasis was laid more and more on worldly matters.

In the Salernitan version which is attributed to Archimatteus much of this was taken over, and through the rapid diffusion of the text became general property. But already by the middle of the twelfth century the more mercenary aspects of medical ethics became prominent and John of Salisbury sarcastically commenting on the students who left Paris to pursue the study of medicine remarked:

But I have noticed that there are two axioms which they are especially fond of, both in theory and practice. The first is from Hippocrates (whom they mistranslate): *Where poverty is, labour is not worth while*, for they consider it foreign to their profession to attend the poor and those who cannot, or will not pay up. Their second maxim does not come, as far as I know, from Hippocrates, but has been concocted by enterprising doctors. It runs: *Take your fee whilst the patient is sick.*

This passage shows that the profession of medicine was not, at this period, in very high repute, at least as regards its ethics. But this was not the whole story. The school of Salerno had made a kind of sumptuary law about the costume to be worn by physicians. Their dress was to be luxurious, they were to wear rings, they were to have a good mount, well harnessed and elaborately equipped, the more to impress the sick man by the appearance of riches and so extort from him a larger sum for medical treatment. A physician of poor aspect would find it difficult to demand a large fee. However, the physicians did not have exclusively rich patients and at Salerno it was the rule to provide medical services for the poor without payment. It was this tradition which encouraged Master Salernus to seek substitutes for the expensive drugs which had to be imported from the East and which led him to draw up a list of simple herbs which could be gathered by the poor in the fields. Thus there grew up a type of medicine which differed greatly from that recommended to the rich, the difference lying not so much in its efficacy as in its taste and appearance. In the *Ars medendi* of Copho, after he had prescribed a vomit composed of fresh sugar and *asaret* mixed with honey, he immediately adds:

Note that the vomit for peasants is briony root crushed to powder.

It was the same in the case of laxatives. For the rich he ordered rhubarb of the finest quality, carefully triturated and infused in hot water, but for the poor he recommended a decoction of plums as being equally effective. Besides this choice there was also a difference in presentation. The rich had their pills gilded because certain drugs were quite repellent to the sight: for the poor it was advised that they be drunk through a straw and in darkness, lest they think they were being given poison. So no matter how charitable the physician might have wished to be, he had to take into account this social inequality and extort from the rich so that he could give more freely to the poor. This was mainly done in demanding high prices for medicines: if the rich wanted pills made of gold, pearls, resins, exotic balm and so forth, they must pay dear for it, especially since to this kind of patient the dearer the drug was, the more potent it appeared. Indeed, the physician was counselled not to be scrupulous in exaggerating the cost:

We usually give things for things, and words for words. For empty
words we give herbs from the hills in exchange, but for precious
money we give spices.

One of the methods peculiar to the Middle Ages was the contract
for payment and cure entered into before medical treatment had
begun. This was based on the sad experience that once the patient
had been cured, he forgot in what straits he had been before the
doctor attended him, and requests for money led to quarrels and
enmity.

When illness overtakes a man, he promises the earth; but when he
has recovered, the doctor is no longer remembered. So demand your
fee the moment you are called in, or at least obtain a pledge.

An interesting contract of this kind is preserved in a Brussels manuscript concerning a physician, John of England, who promised
to cure Bartoluccio de Samartanis for fifty gold florins. The contract stipulated that John should provide medicines, waters, confections, and so on at his own expense, treat the patient for forty days
after convalescence, and cure him so that he could move his hand,
arm and leg, put on his clothes, fasten his shoes and wash himself
with the injured hand. On his side, the patient paid twenty-five
florins down and promised the rest when the cure was complete.

In official documents there are many instances where doctors had
to invoke the law to recover their fees: defaulters were found not
merely among the nobles, but also among prelates and abbots
of great monasteries like Fountains. Says de Mondeville:

There is one class of notoriously bad payers, the nobility and their
households, government officials, judges, baillies and lawyers.

On the other hand, the practice was: no cure, no fee. The patient,
therefore, was fully insured against negligence and could withhold
payment when he was not satisfied. A number of instances are
recorded in the Chancery Courts of refusal to pay when treatment
had been unsuccessful; in most cases the patient's complaints were
accepted.

Medical treatment, however, could be prolonged for the purpose of exacting larger fees. John Mirfield complained about this trick of the physicians and added that often other doctors were brought in for consultation unnecessarily, for even when they could not agree on a course of treatment, they had to be paid. These wiles of the physicians brought them into bad repute and there are many sly digs at them in the poems of the time. The wiles of the patients, however, were no less cunning, and the *Cautions* given by Arnold of Villanova to doctors show to what lengths they would go to bring a physician into disrepute and so deprive him of his practice and his livelihood. In an age when diagnosis of disease was mainly dependent on the inspection of urine many subterfuges were resorted to by patients, either to conceal their social position, their true ailments, their sex, or their ability to pay. Pregnant women would send some old crone to the physician with a urinal for diagnosis, attempting to deceive the physician into thinking that the old woman was the patient. Light white wine would be substituted in order to confuse him, or two different urinals would be sent purporting to belong to the same patient. The physicians had to be as wily as the patients and as cautious in giving advice as circumstances would permit. So Arnold always counselled them to say something ambiguous to outwit their questioners, to spit or blow their noses to gain time, to attribute illnesses to some kind of obstruction, and so on.

What the exact physicians' fees were we have no means of knowing. It is not until quite late in the Middle Ages that we have accounts giving details of such costs. Most of these come from monastic infirmaries where physicians have been called in either to inspect the urine of a sick man, or to prescribe remedies for what can only be surmised were digestive complaints, colds, rheumatic pains and so forth. Usually, the price for the inspection of urine was three shillings and fourpence, but one has to consider that this was sometimes in addition to an annual stipend and the provision of robes. The royal physicians were naturally the best paid of all: not only were they given an annual retainer and robes, but often provided with an annuity until death. Some of them made immense fortunes by dabbling in other business besides medicine, and one of them, Pancio da Controne, was found at his death to be owed £4,000 by the king – a vast fortune in those days. In the case of clerical physicians their rewards were often in the shape of benefices to which they were collated at the royal instance: this saved the king expense and provided ample revenues whose source was always secure.

The doctor's wealth and the social position it gave him also brought other jobs as well. If he was attached to the court, he was often sent on diplomatic missions abroad or given royal errands of a more personal character. Some were placed in charge of the building of the king's castles, and in one instance a physician supervised the erection of the king's country mansion at Clipstone, near Nottingham, where presumably his knowledge of 'geometry', that is, the siting of the house with regard to sun, wind and water, was put to good use. He also laid out the gardens and the fishing ponds. Another was given charge of the king's forests.

The surgeons, however, appear to have been more conscious than the physicians of the earlier rules about ethics and etiquette. Whilst the physician's manuals limit themselves to purely medical matters, the surgeon's treatises almost invariably begin with a chapter on the necessary qualifications, both moral and technical, which the student of surgery should possess. Thus we find in the works of William de Saliceto, Lanfranc, Henri de Mondeville, John Arderne and the later writers on surgery both in England and elsewhere, a preliminary introduction on these matters. Naturally, they all produce the same ideas, sometimes even the same words, but at least it reveals that the retaining of professional standards was always in the forefront of their minds. This is how John of Arderne described his ideal surgeon:

It behoveth him that will profit in this craft that he set God first evermore in his works . . . and sometimes visit of his winnings poor men . . . that they by their prayers may get him grace of the Holy Ghost . . . Be a leech not much laughing nor much playing. And as much as he may without harm, flee the fellowship of knaves and of unhonest persons. Be he evermore occupied in things that beholden his craft, either read he or write he or pray he, for the exercise of books worshippeth a good leech. And above all it profiteth him that he be found sober, for drunkenness destroyeth all virtue and bringeth it to nothing. Scorn he no man: if there be made speech to him of any leech, neither set him at nought nor praise him too much or commend him, but thus may he courteously say: I have no great knowledge of him, but I learned nought, nor have I heard ought of him but good and honest . . . Also dispose the leech that in clothes and other apparellings he be honest, not likening himself to minstrels, but in clothing and bearing shew he the manner of clerks.

He has much else to say in the same vein, and all that regarded behaviour in the presence of women, the rich, the poor and the sick, is treated in the same sober and straightforward fashion.

The surgical writer who has dealt most fully with these details is Mondeville. From the quotation of certain of his remarks, given by various writers, one might gain the impression that he was utterly mercenary. But his attitude was the result of bitter experience.

The rich have a nasty habit of coming to the surgeon in old clothes, or if they come properly dressed, they invent all kinds of excuses for beating down his fees. They say that Charity is a virtue, and think that the surgeon should assist the poor. They never consider that this precept applies to them too. To such folk I always say: If you will pay for three paupers as well as yourself, I will treat you all. To this they give no answer, and I have never found anyone, whether cleric or layman, who will pay what he has promised unless he is forced or taken to law.

Most of what Mondeville has to say concerns unscrupulous surgeons, but he does not let physicians go unscathed. For they employed ignorant men when surgical treatment was required in order that they could assume an appearance of superiority, and when the case was unsuccessfully treated, they took their own fee, blamed the result on the surgeon and tried to bring discredit on their colleagues. They also employed dishonest apothecaries who adulterated the drugs, shared their profits with them and then disclaimed all responsibility for any harm that might ensue.

Previously the supervision of the apothecaries had been in the hands of the physicians. They were supposed to examine stocks of drugs in the apothecaries' shops, report those which had gone stale and lost their therapeutic qualities, and have them burned publicly when necessary. But they failed to stamp out the charlatans who travelled from town to town selling their wares as a universal panacea, and setting up stalls in the markets where they addressed the gaping yokels:

Good people, I am not one of those poor preachers nor one of those poor herbalists who stand in front of the churches with their shabby ill-sewn cloaks, who carry boxes and bags and spread out their wares on a carpet: they sell pepper, cumin and other spices. Know that I am not one of them . . . I belong to a lady called Trotula of Salerno . . . And she sends us out into divers lands and countries, to Apulia and Calabria and Tuscany, Germany, Soissons and Gascony, Spain, Champaigne, Burgundy and the Forest of the Ardennes, to kill beasts and extract ointments from them and to give medicines to those who are sick. I will now teach you how to cure worms, if you will hear me. Will you hear me? Is no gentleman here going to ask me from what worms come? I will tell you. They come from cooked up meats and from wines in casks and bottles; they grow in the body by heat and humours (so the philosophers say) and they mount towards the heart and then you die of a malady that is called sudden death. And the best herb in the world to cure it is Ermoize . . . Take three roots of this, five leaves of plantain, beat them in a brass mortar with an iron pestel and drink the juice for three mornings . . . And because my Lady wishes that the poor should be healthy as well as the rich, she told me to make pennyworths of them, for many a man has a penny in his pocket who has not £5 . . . You must not eat these herbs, for there is no ox or warhorse, be they never so strong, that can bear a piece of these herbs on its tongue but would presently die an evil death, for they are strong and bitter. Steep them three days in good white wine; if you have no white, take red, and if you have no red, take brown, or if you have no brown, take fair clean water, for many a man has a clear well before his door who has not a cask of wine in his cellar. Take it first thing in the morning for thirteen mornings . . . and I tell you by the Passion of God that you will be cured of your disorders and diseases, from quartan fevers, gout, etc. If my father and mother were in peril of death and were to ask me for the herb, I should give them these. This is how I sell my herbs and ointments. If you want them, come and take them: if you don't want them, leave them alone.

Thus does a contemporary in *Ruteboeuf* recall the patter of the itinerant apothecaries and herbalists.

As time progressed the universities took greater and more careful guard over the qualifications of those who wished to enter the medical profession: studies were meticulously graded, degrees were more sparingly awarded and the competence of practitioners was jealously supervised. All the same, the difference in knowledge between the doctors of the early days and the physicians of the fifteenth century was scarcely noticeable and the descriptions of them given by educated and sarcastic laymen show that on the whole they did not hold their attainments in high regard. Chaucer's doctor of physic belongs as much to the twelfth as to the fourteenth century:

> With us ther was a Doctour of phisyck
> In al this world ne was ther noon him lyk
> To speke of phisik and of surgerye ...
> He knewe the cause of everich maladye,
> Were it of hoot or cold, or moiste, or drye,
> And where engendred, and of what humour;
> He was a verrey parfit practisour ...
> Full redy had he his apothecaries,
> To send him drogges and his lectuaries,
> For ech of hem made other for to winne ...

Caxton's, a century later, remains the same figure of tolerant amusement.

Chapter Twelve

Hygiene

It appears to be a general assumption that hygiene in the Middle Ages was almost non-existent. Much capital has been made of the various statutes and decrees emanating from civic councils concerning the filth and refuse that was deposited in the streets, squares, rivers and so forth. But it seems to have escaped attention that these are decrees which *forbid* the fouling of towns and cities. The conclusion to be drawn should be exactly opposite to the one usually made. But before we deal with this topic, the attitude towards personal hygiene, which is even more fundamental, should be considered.

What strikes one as particularly surprising is the number of treatises written during the Middle Ages on what was called the regimen of health. One of the earliest of these, certainly the one which had the greatest circulation in medieval times, was the *Regimen sanitatis* attributed to the school of Salerno. In this little book, which contains a great deal that concerns food, not a little space is devoted to matters of personal cleanliness. Attention is drawn to the necessity of combing the hair, cleaning the teeth, washing, changing one's linen and many other things usually associated with a much later age. Undoubtedly these treatises were aimed at the more educated classes, and it would be forcing the evidence to suppose that all classes, poor and rich alike, had the same opportunities or the same inclination to spend time on personal appearance and cleanliness. But the fact that such ideas were commonly bandied about is proof enough that dirt and filth were not the accepted concomitants of life in a medieval city.

The hygienic regulation of an individual's life began with the pregnant mother. Her food and mode of life were prescribed to suit the unborn child. No food difficult to digest was to be taken: small rather than large meals were advocated, and spiced meats, tarts, and elaborate dishes were to be avoided. Worry and vexation of mind were to be eliminated and an equable temperament was, as far as possible, to be fostered. Before the child was born, a cradle, cloths, hot water and a small basin were prepared. After the umbilical cord had been tied with a thread, a bandage of linen strips soaked in olive oil was wound round the body of the new-born child and it was bathed. All medieval directions to midwives concerning care for mother and child demand that their hands should be clean and their fingernails pared and smoothed so as not to injure the child. Especial care was to be taken to ensure that the child was kept warm, for cold could be most injurious. The child was to sleep apart in a cradle, lest by sleeping with its mother it should be suffocated. To ensure the normal development of the child's limbs, the arms and legs were extended and the child swaddled from head to foot. During the first few days of life it had to lie in complete darkness to protect its eyes from the bright light of day. It was to be bathed two or three times a day, care being taken that no water entered the ears. To make the limbs supple, mild exercises were performed in the bath, such as flexing the knees and touching the feet with the hands. If possible the child was to be suckled by the mother; the breasts were to be washed before feeding, but if the child refused the breast, the nipples were to be smeared with honey.

Weaning took place between the ages of one and two. After weaning, the diet to be followed by the child was prescribed in great detail. To ease teething, to teach the child to walk, to help it to form words, a number of common-sense directions were given. The greatest care was to be taken of the child until it reached the age of seven, when a period of toughening and hardening of the body to prepare it for the physical and martial exercises of later life was entered on.

The medieval health tracts that have survived also inform us about the regulation of adult life. Bodily cleanliness, food and housing were the three subjects included under personal hygiene. Particular attention was paid to the teeth. In order to keep the mouth healthy and to give the breath a pleasant odour, fragrant leaves were chewed, the mouth rinsed with wine in which roots of various herbs had been steeped or boiled, and the teeth themselves brushed with powders, mainly consisting of burnt hartshorn and pulverized marble. Albert the Great gives as a recipe: an ounce of myrrh, two teaspoonfuls of white honey, a little sage well ground up to be used both night and morning.

The hair was also the object of meticulous care. There is scarcely a book on medicine from medieval times which does not include some recipes for colouring the hair, keeping it bright and curly, preventing baldness, and making the eyelashes and eyebrows grow long. Indeed, in a society that evidently placed great emphasis on beauty, the cosmetic arts were intensely cultivated: all kinds of facial cosmetics for preserving and softening the skin, for ridding oneself of pimples and other blemishes, for giving a rosy complexion, for making the eyes clear and bright, and much else, are listed even in such scholastically toned works as those of Gilbertus Anglicus, Arnold of Villanova, John Gaddesden, John Arderne and many others.

Bathing was not so uncommon as has been believed. It is often said that the Church frowned upon the use of baths. But this is a misconception. Bathing in one form or another had always been considered a necessary element in medical care: hot steaming baths, cold baths, herb baths had been prescribed even from Anglo-Saxon times and, though for personal hygiene baths were not taken so frequently as today, they were prescribed for certain times of the year, feast days and so on. When knights were accepted into the ranks of chivalry they were given a bath before their reception, both as a symbol and a real cleansing. Baths were taken after combat, on return from journeys, on coming out of prison, and at many other times. Soap was in use from early times. Gilbertus Anglicus distinguishes several kinds and gives the ingredients for making them. Indeed, in some ways bodily cleanliness was fostered more in these medieval centuries than it was in the sixteenth and seventeenth centuries. Washing facilities, however, for the poor and the ordinary citizen were probably primitive, though the urban population was better provided for than the country dwellers, whose woollen garments, whilst absorbing the sweat produced by their toil, would also house lice and other parasites, which if not cleared away by constant washing would cause skin irritation. The medical treatises of the times take it for granted that lice, fleas, insects of all kinds, both in the hair, on the body, in the ears and sometimes in the eyes, were common. The odour of unwashed bodies is tacitly accepted as a common factor in the recipes for *pomum ambre*, a device carried about by the wealthy as they walked the streets or attended public services in churches and halls to dispel the stink. Cardinal Wolsey always carried one.

Washing was dependent on a plentiful water supply, and a lack of this may have encouraged many people to take a 'dry stew' rather than a wet one. There were a number of public stews to which the less wealthy could resort, constantly and carefully supervised by the authorities. Men and women had to go to separate houses, each one having a bath keeper in charge. No laundry was allowed to be taken inside, so that the bath would always remain clean for the bathers.

Though we are well informed about the kind and variety of food which went to the tables of the kings and nobles of the time, we are not so certain about the diet of the ordinary working man. From the accounts of the royal household it is easy to garner a list of foods that were placed before the king and his servants. Apart from the usual staple foods like bread, ale, cheese and eggs, a large variety of fish, both salted and fresh, was used: bream, cod, conger eels, herrings, lampreys, mullet, pike, salmon, sturgeon. Meat appears to have been in plentiful supply: beef, boars' flesh, pork, mutton, porpoise meat, rabbits, venison and all kinds of game that could be caught in the king's forests. We hear little of fresh vegetables, the main greens being peas and beans. Most of these foods were not fresh because they had to be brought long distances to the king's table, and since he was often on the move from one town to another, the fish and meat had to be stored in some convenient place to be used on his arrival. Enormous amounts of these foods had to be salted down or made into pies and paste, and there are lists for the years in the middle of the thirteenth century when over a thousand carcases of bacon, 20,000 eels, 500 congers and so on were ordered to be salted down. In some cases the amount of money allowed for the salting of these incredible amounts of fish and meat seems quite inadequate and it is possible that a certain amount of the food would not have kept good for very long. Since much of it, particularly in the castles, was intended to supply the garrison for many months at a time, one can only surmise that in many ways the diet was deficient.

For the poor the choice was naturally much more restricted.

> Bread and thin ale for them are a banquet,
> Cold flesh and cold fish are like roast venison,
> A farthing's worth of mussels, a farthing's worth of cockles,
> Were a feast for them on Friday or fast-days.

A writer in the mid-fourteenth century, contrasting the diet of the rich and poor, makes these comparisons:

> Wouldst thou have lords to live as lads a-foot?
> Proud merchants of price, as pedlars o' the village?
> Let lords live as they list, lads as befits them, –
> These the bacon and beef, these (the rich) bitterns and swans,
> These the rough of the rye, these the ruddy wheat,
> These the gray gruel, these the good sauce;
> So may the people have their part, now in poverty bested,
> Some good morsel of meat to mend their ill cheer.

In both these quotations there is a certain element of propaganda, an emphasis on the great gulf between the food habits of the rich and poor, but there is also evidence that even the peasants had good, if not rich fare. In the Nativity Play where the Adoration of the Shepherds was dramatized, we find the following lines, which appear to indicate that wholesome food was available to the workers on the land:

> Here is bread this day was baken
> Onyons, Garlik, and lyckes,

butter that bought was in Blacon
and greene cheese that will grease your cheekes ...
lo – here a sheepes head souced in ale,
and a groyne to lay on the grene,
and soure mylke my wife had on sale ...
And that is my sachell to shake out
to shepheards am I not ashamed:
this Oxe tonge, pared round about,
for your tooth it shall be attamed.

The drink of the richer classes was, in general, wine. In the royal accounts there are numerous references to wines of various kinds and it would appear that practically the whole of France was scoured to secure the best vintages available. There are references to wine from Anjou, Auxerre (Burgundy), Bordeaux, Gascony, La Rochelle, Le Blanc, St Jean d'Angely, Taillebourg, Bergerac, Chatellrault, Moissac, Touraine; there were clove-scented wines, raspberry and mulberry flavoured wines, iron impregnated wines, honeyed wines. These were kept in many places in the country, wherever the king might visit, and the cellars are mentioned at Geddington, Kempton, Kingscliffe, Marlborough, Northampton, Southampton, Westminster, Windsor, Woodstock, besides many castles up and down the country. At times of feasting these wines were spiced by the royal physician or apothecary and often it would appear that this was the only function that the king's physician had to perform.

For the lower classes ale was the staple drink. It varied in strength; one gallon a day was the usual allowance for labourers on monastic or Lord's lands. It was usually brewed by women who kept ale houses, though a certain amount was brewed at home for the consumption of the family. The demand for it was great and as usual there were the addicts who would pledge anything to get it:

Som bryngeth her husbandes hood,
Because the ale is good:
Another brought her his cap
To offer to the ale tap,
With flax and wyth towe;
Some brought sowre dowe; ...

> *Some layde to pledge*
> *Theyr hatchett and theyr wedge*
> *Theyr hekell and theyr rele,*
> *Theyr rock, and theyr spynnyng whele;*
> *And some went so narrowe,*
> *They layde to pledge theyr wharrowe,*
> *Theyr rybskyn and theyr spyndell*
> *Theyr nedell and theyr thymbell.* . . .

All these implements are those used in the processes for turning flax into yarn, for many housewives spun the yarn necessary for the linen of the house.

One of the reasons for the great drinking of ale was the unsuitability of the water because of its lack of purity and its comparative inaccessibility. It was certainly safer to drink water after it had passed through the brewing process in which it was boiled. Many people considered that to drink water was fraught with danger, especially in Springtime when it was 'thycke with vapours than ben resolved and shed', and when it was 'infect with frogges and other wormes that than brede'. It was therefore considered necessary to drink it only when it had been 'cleansed and pourged by boyllynge'.

All boroughs possessed public wells, some of which were extremely ancient and of social and religious significance. These were found mostly at cross-roads or near churches. In some towns taxes were imposed on those who drew water from the common well. Stow describes London during the two hundred years after the Conquest as having 'in everie street and lane of the Citie diverse fayre welles and fresh springs; and after this manner was the citie then served, with sweete and fresh waters'.

For industrial purposes, the river which often ran through or round the city was the source of water supply. The brewers, dyers and tanners often settled near the water's edge in order to carry on their trade. But this invariably led to pollution and rendered the water unfit for human consumption. Since also the river was, in most cases, the only means of getting rid of garbage and rubbish of all kinds, it became a public dumping-ground. The butchers and fishmongers threw their offal into it, the washerwomen cleansed their sheets, garments and other linen in it, sewage was piped into it, and in general it became more a public sewer than a source of clean and wholesome water. As time progressed legislation was enforced to prevent this wholesale pollution of the rivers, but as other means of water supply were slow in coming, the nuisance persisted until well into the fifteenth century. Already in the thirteenth century the supply of water to buildings of importance, such as the royal palaces and castles, was being facilitated by the use of pipes. In the royal accounts there are many references to cisterns, fountains, conduits and so on being introduced to various halls and rooms: at Westminster pipes were laid to carry away the garbage from the kitchens to the Thames because the king and his entourage could not bear the stench of filthy water being carried through the main halls in which they gathered. Gradually this process became widespread. But in the towns it was the religious Orders, such as the Franciscan and Dominican Friars, who began the tradition of building conduits from unpolluted springs to supply their houses. Following their lead, cities like London, Bristol and Coventry began to build conduits. Though the advantages of conduits over public wells were considerable, the higher costs involved in installing them were a great deterrent, and town authorities were slow to follow their lead; but in many instances the Friars and the town councils came to amicable arrangements whereby, in exchange for undertaking to keep the conduits in constant repair, the townspeople were allowed to use the Friars' water. The convenience of water conduits was great. Water led through pipes either of wood or lead could be made to emerge at the most convenient points for the townspeople's use: it was almost completely free from contamination, its flow could be controlled and it guaranteed that many people could be supplied simultaneously.

As a rule victuallers were forbidden to use this water for their trade. To counteract abuses, even of householders, regulations were drawn up and a special keeper of the conduit appointed. At Coventry a law was enacted that 'grates and lokkes be made to loke withall the Cundites in the nyght'. A charge at the conduits for the use of water was imposed in London for at least a century after their establishment, but to what extent ordinary citizens in other places had to contribute to their upkeep is not known.

In London there was a professional class called 'the Brotherhood of St Christopher of the Waterbearers', whose duty it was to take water round to various households in much the same way as the milkman does today. Each member had a fixed round on which no other waterbearer could encroach, neither could a member entice a customer away from another, 'without so be that the parties that he serveth will no longer have his service, and that the said brother seith that he be content of his diewte that he should have'.

Among the victuals ordered for the king's use there is rarely mention of fruit. The only fruits that appear in the lists are figs, raisins, dates and almonds; there is no mention of apples, pears, peaches, mulberries, raspberries, strawberries, cherries and plums. This has given rise to the assumption that there was little fruit in medieval England and that for the most part it was frowned upon as an article of diet by the physicians. It is true that the *Regimen Salernitanum,* which discusses various foods in detail, advises against eating certain fruits because they affect the digestion or breed melancholy humours, but the prohibition was not absolute and a great number of fruits is listed and recommended. The fruits for the king's table were generally of the more costly kind, fruits that had to be imported from abroad and which therefore possessed a certain *cachet* not to be associated with the more common products of the ordinary English garden. But cherries, apples and plums were to be easily obtained and even the poor could procure them, for Piers Plowman speaks of their bringing him 'baken apples' and 'cherries'. Many fruits grew wild and were available even to the poorest, for we read that in 1460–71 William Wight and his wife Isabella were amerced for collecting crab apples and wild apples on Wimbledon Common. Most of these fruits were known in Anglo-Saxon times, and in the Leech Books there are references to apples, pears, peaches, medlars, plums and cherries.

One of the earliest descriptions of a garden is that by Alexander Neckham, written in the second half of the twelfth century. A garden, he says, should have on one side roses, lilies, heliotrope, violets, mandrakes: on the other, parsley cost, fennel, southernwood, coriander, sage, savory, hyssop, mint, rue, dittany, smallage, pellitory, lettuce, garden cresses and peony. There should also be beds of onions, leeks, garlic, pumpkins, shallots and cucumber. Nor should the pot-herbs be forgotten, such as beet, mallow, herbmercury and orache. There should be mustard, white pepper and wormwood. He then goes on to list the fruit trees: medlars, quinces, peaches, pears, lemons, oranges, pomegranates, almonds, dates and figs. Some of these, of course, were not cultivated in northern climates, but he evidently thought that, where possible, they should be grown. The vineyard was also an important adjunct to the medieval mansion, though Neckham fails to say anything about its culture in this country.

In the monasteries the establishment of herb gardens had been known from time immemorial. The ninth-century plan of St Gall gives an outline of the garden with the specific herbs to be grown there for the use of the infirmarian. This tradition was certainly carried on throughout the Middle Ages, for until relaxations in diet were allowed after the Black Death, most of the religious Orders were completely vegetarian. Meat and fish were not allowed at their tables, except on special occasions, so that they were wholly dependent on what they could grow in their fields and gardens. The presence in their libraries of the classical treatise, Palladius' *De agricultura*, indicates the interest they had in the cultivation of fruit and vegetables. The Rolls of the gardener at Worcester Cathedral Priory show that, besides the usual vegetables, they also grew apples, plums and cherries for their own consumption; whilst the Rental Book of Cupar Abbey in Fife even gives detailed instructions to the monastic tenants about the type and the amount of vegetables they must grow on their plots of land.

Housing conditions were not always ideal. Even in the castles and palaces of the rich the walls and floors were damp, due to condensation on the stone structure and inadequate heating facilities. The majority of London houses were built of wood and thatched with straw, reeds or stubble; but the great fire which, beginning at London Bridge, destroyed St Paul's Cathedral and all the houses as far as St Clement Danes, led the more opulent citizens to use free-stone with tiles for roofs. The covering of the floors was mainly rushes or straw, on which the bones and remains of food from the table were thrown to the dogs and in which vermin thrived. Lighting was a problem, for windows were merely holes in the walls to be covered up with curtains or wooden shutters. Glass was far too expensive for the ordinary household and only important buildings, like churches, monasteries, and municipal guildhalls, could afford it. Illumination was provided by lamps filled with fat or fish oil, whose fumes irritated the mucous membranes of eyes and nose; whilst heating depended on wood and peat fires, the smoke from which could escape through large vents in the houses of the wealthy, but swirled about the room in the ordinary peasant dwelling. Chaucer has described the cottage of a widow in the following words:

> *Ful sooty was hir bour, and eek hire halle,*
> *In which she eet ful many a sclendre meel....*

The hygiene of the towns was a different and more complex matter than that of the individual. After the beginning of the twelfth century, urban centres grew rapidly as a result of increasing prosperity and expansion of trade. Many of them could no longer house within their ancient boundaries the increasing population, and chronic overcrowding was widespread. This brought in its train problems of sanitation. With the increase of craftsmen of all kinds with the consequent production of waste from their activities, the dumping of refuse outside their shops, forges, slaughter houses and mills became common. Also the more wealthy burghers, who possessed horses for transport with stables for their shelter, did not hesitate to dispose of their straw, dung, and other refuse by throwing it into the common highway. The town authorities did not willingly tolerate this state of affairs and attempts were always being made to force careless and ignorant citizens to desist from these insanitary practices. Judging by the number and severity of municipal laws concerning the cleansing of the streets more credit should be given to the townsfolk of the Middle Ages for their awareness of the dangers that arose from these bad habits.

What the rubbish and filth was that was too frequently allowed to accumulate in the streets, is usually described in borough ordinances and the charges brought against tradesmen and private householders. The cleaning out of stables and the emptying of their contents on to the streets caused most annoyance and nuisance. In Edward II's time the Corporation of London forbade any citizen to throw dust, dung, sawdust, straw or other refuse into the streets and lanes. The throwing of water, the contents of urinals and other noisome liquids from windows was another source of trouble, mostly carried out by servants, hostlers and cooks, who were too lazy to dispose of it otherwise.

Butchers were notorious for befouling the public ways. They slaughtered their beasts openly in the streets, leaving the entrails and offal on the cobblestones and pavements. At Northampton the butchers were expressly forbidden to cast offal 'such as lightis, longis hornes and other annoyable thyngis behind the stalls or on the pavement'. Poulterers, too, sinned in this respect. A lengthy complaint of London citizens to the Mayor draws attention to the behaviour of poulterers as being 'a grete and noyous and grevous hurt', since they persisted in using the public highway for 'swannes, gees, heron-ewes and other pultrie, whereof the ordure and standyng of hem is of grete stenche and so evel savour that it causeth grete and parlous infectyng of the people and long hath done'. As they plucked the dead birds in the streets, the whirling feathers constituted another nuisance. When they did not cast their rubbish into the streets, they employed women to carry entrails away in baskets, who thereupon deposited their loads at the gates of the towns, thus merely removing the nuisance from one public place to another.

The committing of nuisances in the streets by townspeople, particularly at night, was common. But as early as 1299 two officials were appointed in London to watch the streets and prevent this as far as possible. There was, however, no general policy or organisation for dealing with the cleansing of towns, and it was only when the outbreak of disease or the visit of some great personage like the king forced them, that the authorities tried to come to grips with the problem. The first step was usually to ensure that each house-

holder kept the street clean outside his own house. But as neighbours were apt to sweep their dirt in front of the next house,
quarrels were frequent and gave rise to litigation and sometimes to
violence. To enforce the observance of this statute an official was
appointed, and sometimes an official sweeper and carter, to supervise this matter. The heaps of rubbish in front of each house were
allowed to remain for seven days at least, because Saturday was
fixed as the day for cleaning in preparation for the sabbath day.
The refuse could perhaps have been destroyed by burning, but in
the close, narrow streets, with their timber houses, the fires of straw
and dung constituted a grave danger and could have led to disaster.
As time progressed, the period of time between each collection of
refuse became shorter, so that by the fifteenth century some towns
allowed the heaps to stand for two nights only.

The men appointed to deal with the removal of rubbish were
called scavengers, holding their position under the beadle of the
ward. There was also a 'surveyor' whose duty it was to impose fines
for fouling the streets. In London a further class of men called
'rakyers' was formed, elected annually in each ward, to call at each
house and carry away the accumulated muck. But the final disposal
of rubbish presented a very grave problem.

At first the town or river had been frequently used for this
purpose, but with the growing populations and the increasing
volume of filth the rivers were unable to absorb all the waste
matter: they became contaminated and a source of disease.
Already in the fourteenth century prohibitions against unloading
rubbish into the town streams and rivers had been made by various
bodies. At York, the butchers built a pier over the River Ouse in
1371 from which to throw their offal, but two years earlier the
London butchers had been ordered to stop this for fear of polluting
the Thames. Bochersbridge, which they had previously used for
this purpose, was pulled down. In certain towns dumping grounds
were assigned for this purpose, but in London the offal of slaughtered beasts was supposed to be buried.

There still remained the problem of disposal of sewage, which
from its nature could not be solved merely by removing it from the
centre of the towns. In some places latrines were built, but not

enough mention of them is made in Borough records to enable us to assess the extent to which this was done. At Leicester the Dominican friars tried to persuade the public from using certain latrines because they were situated on ground which they wanted for their own use. They therefore gave money to the city to build one elsewhere and a plot of land, donated by the Earl of Leicester. Both sites appear to have been situated on the outskirts of the borough, near the river, so possibly they were drained into it. But owing to the redistribution of population the position of some of these public latrines became a danger to health: the latrine, for instance, between All Hallows and Bishopsgate was pulled down and removed to a site outside the walls of the city. The danger was increased by the difficulty of connecting water with these latrines. Small streams and ditches could not be put to this use indefinitely, for they contaminated the water supply. As early as 1355 complaints had been made of the contamination of the water supply near Fleet prison and shortly after Walbrook itself was regarded as a public danger. Not until 1462 was it cleaned up, paved and vaulted to prevent people, who owned property along the ditch, from setting up 'seges'. These householders were then ordered to carry out the work along their own frontage as far as the middle of the brook, and in 1477 it was forbidden to set up any 'sege' over Walbrook or any town ditch. This regulation ultimately prevailed, and Stow could say later: 'This water course having divers bridges was afterwards vaulted over with bricks, and paved levell with the Streetes and Lanes where through it passed . . . so that the course of Walbrooke is now hidden under ground and thereby hardly knowne.' An attempt was made also to provide a periodic cleansing and clearing of the public pits, and in 1466 a contract was made for the clearing of all privies within the City and liberties for a period of ten years. Much the same solution was found at Coventry and elsewhere.

The cleansing of the streets depended a great deal on the extent to which they were paved. Where the streets were made of hard earth, having no covering of stones or cobbles, bad weather, storms, frost and such like could reduce the highway into a bog. In 1300 the streets of Oxford were in such a deplorable state that a levy was imposed on the clergy for their improvement, their terrible effects on epidemics having been realised. Not until a century later did London follow this example. In the case of Canterbury the accounts for paving the city survive. A special Act of Parliament was granted empowering the Corporation to pave the horse roads and to raise a levy to pay the cost. The first part was begun in 1480 extending from All Saints Church to King's Bridge; then followed Fish Street. Each owner was ordered to pave the part in front of his property. In 1485 the main drain was constructed; in 1499 the road to King's Mead was repaired, though this involved only the laying down of faggots of broom to fill the ruts caused by passing traffic. Fines were exacted for fouling the streets but with little or no effect, for in 1505 it was reported that 'for lacke of carriage of the myre. [they are] foul and full of myre, to the grete dishonour of the Citie, and the greet damage of the inhabitants by corrupte and infestuous heiers'. A common carrier was ordered to go through the streets and remove all offal, dust and other corruption 'in every house, all manner of horse-donge excepted'.

The process, therefore, of establishing some kind of standard of hygiene in the cities was slow. It had to be enforced in the face of passive resistance from various interested bodies, mostly tradesmen and craftsmen, and was only gradually recognized as necessary by the bulk of the population as a result of a series of epidemics and plagues which brought havoc, destruction and misery in their wake.

Chapter Thirteen

Epidemics

During the Middle Ages the people of Europe were subjected to a succession of epidemics such as has never been experienced before or since. In accordance with the beliefs of the age these plagues were attributed to various causes: the movements of the stars, storms, failure of crops, the effects of drought or floods, swarms of insects, or even to the poisoning of the wells by Jews. The real causes were much less picturesque: namely the crowded conditions of the towns, lack of proper sanitation, bad or rotten food, and in general a prevailing ignorance of true hygiene. For nearly a thousand years the population of Europe was constantly decimated by the recurrence of one or other of these plagues and little could be done, apart from legislation segregating the sick from the healthy, to abate the ravages they caused. At such times men placed more faith in the intercession of the saints than in prophylactic measures, and as a result prayer and pilgrimages were accounted more likely to bring relief than recourse to physicians and their medical remedies.

From the ninth century onwards there are numerous references, especially in France, to what was called St Anthony's fire. This was a form of erysipelas due to the formation of a fungus upon rye, the common staple bread of the poorer classes. The disease usually began with sensations of extreme coldness in the affected part, followed by intense burning pains; a crop of blisters broke out, the limb became livid, foul and putrescent and eventually dropped off. Recovery usually followed the loss of a limb and sometimes patients survived the loss of both arms and legs. About the middle of the eleventh century when this scourge attacked the Dauphiné, one of the most prosperous regions of France, a hospital was built for those afflicted by the disease and a religious Order was founded to tend the stricken. As their church possessed a relic of St Anthony, brought from Constantinople by Josselin de Courtenay, the Order was called the Antonines. One of their most famous hospitals was situated at Vienne, which was visited by St Hugh of Lincoln whilst on his way to Grenoble. His biographer gives the following description of it:

> He turned aside on his journey to the Grande Chartreuse and went a three days' journey to the shrine of St Anthony, where the 'infernal fire' . . . is by some invisible power deprived of its effects. There, we saw not one or two, but hundreds of marvels greater than we had seen anywhere else. For we saw youths and maidens, old and young, cured of the 'sacred fire', some with their flesh eaten away, others with their bones completely destroyed, others still, having lost one or other of their limbs, living a normal life, as if their attenuated frames were sound and whole. . . . What is most extraordinary about these cures is that once the disease has ceased to affect the patient's limbs, the skin and members eaten away by the disease are not restored. And what is more remarkable still is that where the bones have been laid bare, the scars on the rest of the body are so sound and healthy that you can see people of all ages of both sexes with their arms eaten away from wrist to elbow, or from elbow to shoulder, or with legs rotted from ankle to knees, or even to their abdomen, going about actively as if there was nothing wrong with them at all. And so completely does the power of the Saint compensate for their lost members, that even if they have lost skin and flesh from their ribs, the sensitive internal organs feel no discomfort from cold. And so . . . they go about with their scars, a living testimony to the plague, to the skill of their Physician, an object of fear, but an encouragement to devotion.

But it was not all a question of prayers and miracles. Real medical attention was given at the hospital. There was a staff of surgeons to attend the sick – surgical instruments from the earliest times survive as a proof – and if gangrene did not automatically mortify the limbs of the patient, the Antonines used a bistouri to cut off the affected parts. These members, which were excised to prevent the virus from spreading, went black, hardened and became, as it were, incorruptible. These limbs were preserved and hung up in the church as a kind of *ex-voto* to the patron saint of the hospital, without any precaution being made to preserve them by artificial means. In 1639, when Dom Durand and Don Martène, two celebrated Maurists, visited the hospital at Vienne, they recorded:

> We saw a number of those whose limbs had been cut off. Some of them had no feet, others had no hands, and some had neither hands nor feet. One of the brethren in attendance showed us limbs that had been cut off more than a hundred years earlier, and they were just like those that are cut off at the present day, that is to say, they are black and shrivelled.

No less devastating in its effects and certainly more disgusting in its appearance was leprosy. In the sixth and seventh centuries, probably as a result of Saracen invasions into Spain, it began to make its appearance in northern Europe, and so rapid was its increase that leper hospitals for the segregation of the affected soon became a necessary precaution to halt the spread of the disease. Whether the disease was true leprosy or not has been debated, but the description of the symptoms handed down by contemporary physicians is sufficiently appalling to make one see the aptness of choosing Job, as did some leper hospitals, as their patron 'for from the sole of his foot to the crown of his head there was no soundness in him'.

According to Gilbertus Anglicus, the eyebrows and lashes fell off, the nose and features became thick, course and lumpy, the face lost its mobility and play of expression, the eyes were unseeing and unsightly, the voice became raucous, the limbs were so maimed and stunted that the sufferer could but hobble or crawl. Apart from the strong feelings of repulsion that such symptoms aroused, the fear of contagion and the inability to discover any effective remedy led the people of the Middle Ages to adopt the only means at their disposal, the complete isolation of the leper. Before this could take place, an ecclesiastical judge (like the Priests in the Old Testament) had to examine the suspect for signs of the disease, and if he was found contagious and infectious, he was banned from town and

L

byway to some solitary spot remote from the homes of healthy citizens. There was a special ritual for this, headed by a rubric, and the manner of banishing a leper from the world, differed only slightly from the Office for the dead. After the leper had heard Mass, he put on a sombre garment, took a bell or clapper in his hand to warn passers-by of his approach and then set off to the hut assigned to him in the countryside, an outcast from human society. When the number of lepers to be isolated became considerable, their huts were grouped in a kind of enclosure, and if circumstances permitted, buildings in stone were substituted, with dormitories, refectories and halls where they could gather together for social intercourse. It is estimated that by the thirteenth century there were more than two thousand such leper houses in Europe.

One of the most curious epidemics to appear in the Middle Ages was called St Vitus' dance. Crowds of people were suddenly smitten with an urge to dance and, though they professed to be suffering agonies whilst doing so, continued their compulsive movements for long periods at a time, even until they fell down and died. There are many descriptions from contemporary authors of these epidemics, and one of the most vivid, as also one of the earliest, comes from the pen of Giraldus Cambrensis, who gives an account of what happened at Saint Almedha's church in Brecknockshire, South Wales.

The saint's day was celebrated again in the same place where it had been celebrated for many years. The day was August 1st. Many people came here from distant parts, their bodies weakened by various diseases, hoping to be healed through the merits of the holy maiden . . . Men and women could be seen in the church and churchyard, singing and dancing. Suddenly they would fall down quite motionless, as if in a trance, and then as suddenly leap up again like lunatics to perform tasks that were forbidden on feast days . . . One man appeared to have a ploughshare in his hands, another urged forward his oxen with a whip. They accompanied these tasks with songs, but the notes were all out of tune. You could see one imitating a cobbler, another a carpenter; one pretended to be carrying a yoke, whilst another moved his hands as if he were drawing out thread and winding it into a skein. One man would be walking up and down weaving a net with imaginary thread; another one would sit at an imaginary loom, throwing his shuttle to and fro and banging the treadle with jerky movements. Inside the church (which is more surprising), you could see the same people offering gifts at the altar, after which they appeared to rouse themselves from their trance and recover.

Outbreaks of the same epidemic occurred in several other places in Europe, notably at Maastricht in 1278. The *Chronicle of Metz* describes what happened in Germany in 1374:

Those who were most at ease
Became the most afflicted,
Whether sleeping or waking;
Whether sick or poor,
When fate struck home
Then one must dance.
The priest performing the Mass,
The judges who sat in court,
The labourer at his task;
Whomsoever the plague did strike,
He needs must dance for nine or ten days,
Without eating, without rest. . . .

These extraordinary phenomena were witnessed in succeeding centuries, even down to the nineteenth century. There is no doubt that they were due to some physical degeneracy, but, in an age which understood little of these things, it was regarded as demoniac in origin and its victims considered to be possessed of the devil. The cure, therefore, could be obtained only by exorcisms and religious rites. A survival both of the dances and their reputed cure can be seen to this day at Echternach in Luxembourg, where a procession of dancers, singing litanies and prayers, gathers round the tomb of St Willibrord, the Anglo-Saxon missionary, who first brought Christianity to these regions.

The greatest scourge of the Middle Ages was undoubtedly the Black Death which carried off about a quarter – or perhaps even more – of the population of Europe. This disease which began in Constantinople in 1347 had spread, within a year, to Southern France, Italy and Spain, bringing panic and confusion in its train. All restrictions of morality, decency and humanity broke down, and in order to escape it, parents forsook their children, men took ship and fled overseas, whilst those who had no means of travelling gave themselves up to sensual indulgence or, at the opposite extreme, fasted and prayed at the sanctuaries.

Guy de Chauliac, who was then in the service of Pope Clement VI at Avignon, has left us a description of the disease, which, he says, began with a fever and was followed by swellings in the armpits and the groin. Those who fell victims to it usually died within five days:

> It was so contagious, especially if accompanied with the spitting of blood, that not only by staying together, but even by looking at one another, people caught it, with the result that men died without medical attention and were buried without religious rites. The father did not visit his son, nor the son his father. Charity was dead, and hope crushed.

The swellings that Guy de Chauliac mentions as appearing in the armpits and groin were enlarged and infected lymph glands. A gland so infected is called a bubo, hence the term bubonic plague. When a person had the bubonic plague, the glands were not only swollen, but if the patient lived long enough, they also became filled with pus, broke and made running sores.

It is possible that this plague was brought to England in the autumn of 1348 by men fleeing from Calais to escape it. 'It passed,' wrote Robert of Avesbury, contemporary Registrar of the Court of Canterbury, 'most rapidly from place to place, swiftly killing ere mid-day many who in the morning had been well ... On the same day twenty, forty, sixty, and very often more corpses were committed to the same grave.' Starting from Melcombe Regis, the contagion spread quickly over Dorset, Devon and Somerset and the other counties which formed the dioceses of Salisbury, Exeter and Wells. By the end of the year it had reached London. Here the pestilence wrought havoc, helped on by the unsanitary conditions of the city: narrow, ill-cleansed streets, ditches and streams filled with garbage, sewage disposal neglected, bad and corrupt food being sold in the markets. Stowe says that in one cemetery 50,000 corpses were buried, though this figure has been queried by Creighton; but there can be no doubt that the constant assertion of the chroniclers, that the dead outnumbered the living and that there were insufficient healthy people left to carry the corpses to the grave, is no exaggeration. The reports from the religious houses, where the number of inmates was definitely stated, bears this out. At Meaux in Yorkshire 'this pestilence so prevailed in our monastery ... that in the month of August the abbot, twenty-two monks and six lay brethren died; of these the abbot and five monks were lying unburied on one day alone, so that when the plague ceased, out of fifty monks and lay brethren, only ten monks and no lay bretheren survived'. Many country towns were left without inhabitants and in the large cities some quarters were completely depopulated.

The social and economic consequences of this terrible visitation were sudden and revolutionary. The effect on art, education and industry was no less paralyzing: many churches and noble buildings were left unfinished, the universities were almost deserted, and the manufacture of certain things ceased or changed its course. Only in one respect did the plague bring about beneficial results, making the general public aware of the danger of the unsanitary conditions that had previously prevailed. From this time forward we find not only a growing agitation among citizens against the pollution of the streets and water courses, but also an increasing number of publications, both private and public, drawing attention to the way in which contagion of any kind could be avoided. Though plagues of various kinds were to break out in later years, in 1361, 1369, 1371 and 1391, to speak only of the fourteenth century, each time there was a public outcry and the butchers were named as the chief culprits. Not only did they suffer convictions for selling bad meat, characterized as 'putrid, rotten, stinking and an abomination to mankind', but they were banned from slaughtering animals in the cities, where they allowed blood to run down the streets, cast entrails into the rivers and poisoned the air with the stench of decaying offal. In London the slaughtering of beasts could only be carried out at Stratford or Knightsbridge, all entrails had to be scoured before being brought for sale in the city, and any infringement was punished by forfeiture of the cattle and imprisonment for one year. Though this legislation was first passed in

1361, it took thirty years and the threat of a fine of £1,000 to be imposed on the Mayor and sheriffs, before it could be strictly enforced.

Though it is clear both from royal enactments and borough regulations that people were conscious of the relationship between these insanitary practices and the incidence of disease and pestilence, few, if any, medical writers of the times placed any emphasis on it. Bernard Gordon, as we have seen, advised the military physician and surgeon to pitch their tents away from polluted streams, rotting vegetation, corpses and suchlike because of the danger of epidemics; but all the writers who produced plague tracts after the catastrophe of the Black Death appear to have sheered away from this aspect of the problem. True, they counselled the avoidance of pestilential airs, the keeping away from cemeteries, the segregation from infected persons. But in none of them is there any specific mention of purely sanitary measures. Indeed, the prevailing opinion appears to have been that the outbreak of plague had been occasioned by meteorological phenomena, the conjunction of Jove and Saturn, and other uncontrollable forces.

The most widely known and read treatise on the preservation from plague was that attributed to John of Burgundy, written about the year 1365. It was translated, abridged, rehashed in many forms for more than a century, and appeared under various names. Here, in the introduction, we meet the prevailing opinion among medical men regarding the origin of epidemics:

> Alle thynges here in erthe as wele the elementes as thynges sprungen and compowndyd of the elementes ben governed and ledde by the bodyes that ben above in the Spherys or cercles of the firmament.

The atmosphere itself is a simple, incorruptible element, but the evil influences from on high give rise to corrupt vapours which mingle with the atmosphere and cause epidemics. But this is not sufficient of itself to cause pestilence: it depends on the corrupt humours in the human body. Therefore, account must be taken of individual humours, and the diagnosis of a particular disease must not rely on purely theoretical presuppositions, but must be based on practical knowledge of the patient's temperament. There are, however, certain general rules which must be followed by all who wish to avoid contracting the plague.

The first of these concerned regimen: one's life must be sober, abstemious and in all things temperate. Luxury of any kind was to be avoided, but above all hot baths should not be taken lest, by opening up the pores of the skin, the pestilential air should enter and infect the whole body. Diet was to be light: fruit should not be eaten, no food was to be cooked in honey, wine should be drunk sparingly, but vinegar could be mixed with everything. To keep the air inside the house free from infection various aromatic herbs were to be burned on the fire, and windows were to be closed in cold weather. Besides these precautions, certain internal remedies were to be taken, mostly powders from dittany, pimpernel, tormentil, roses and violets, drunk in a glass of wine, but also pills containing cicotrine aloes, fumitory, myrrh, crocus and other ingredients, which destroyed the poisonous vapours which had infiltrated through the pores.

But the most effective method of warding off the plague was by blood-letting. This is how it is described in a letter sent by the masters and doctors of Oxford to the Mayor of London:

If you feel a rushing or pricking of the blood in any part of the body, let blood immediately from the vein nearest to that side; for instance, if an ulcer appears or is felt near the right, immediately draw blood from the right arm and not from the left. And this for two reasons, first, lest the good blood in the left arm should be drawn away; second, lest the poisoned blood pass through the region of the heart from the right arm to the left, and so poison the heart and kill you. This extraction of blood should be made from the vein which is called *cordiata*. But if you feel a pricking or have an ulcer near the ear or the throat, take blood from the arm on that side, that is, from the cephalic vein, or from the vein between the thumb and first finger, or scarify the flesh between the shoulders. But if you have an ulcer in the groin, then open a vein in the foot between the big toe and its neighbour; if the ulcer spreads up the side towards the heart, then open a vein near the heel or scarify the flesh on the leg where the swelling is. If pricking is felt on the right side where the liver is, blood should be taken from the right arm, from the basilic vein or from the vein between the ring and third ('medical') finger. At all events, blood-letting should be carried out when the plague first strikes, whether it be day or night, whether fasting or not, but within six hours; in any event it should not be delayed for more than twelve hours, because then the poisoned blood begins to clot, the disease takes hold and danger of death is imminent.

Various electuaries are recommended for strengthening the body after venesection and for cooling the fever, to be followed by drinks, a plaster, powders and pills.

All this material, though supposedly emanating from the university authorities at Oxford, is taken from John of Burgundy. The same may be said for the treatise, *De remediis spiritualibus et corporalibus contra pestilentiam,* written by John Malverne, chaplain of Balliol, Oxford, later physician to Richard Medford, Bishop of Salisbury, and to King Henry IV. His treatise was prompted by the affixing to church doors of a proclamation giving advice to the common people on how to guard against the plague that was then raging. He did not agree with the recommendation to provoke vomiting and considered it much healthier to avoid over-eating and drunkenness: he advised abstinence from wine, sweet fruits, such as honey and figs, milk, cheese, bad fish, and from heating foods such as beans, oats and garlic. Violent exercise, like running and rough games, should be avoided, as should also hot baths and sleeping after meals. Houses should be filled with sweet scents of roses, violets, bay-leaves, fennel, mint and other aromatic herbs. The remedies mentioned by John of Burgundy were again prescribed, though he thought cicotrine aloes very expensive and much too bitter and nauseous for those with delicate stomachs. On the whole, he was inclined to advise people to flee from places where the plague was rampant, but he could not eliminate from his mind the words of the prophet: 'Whither shall I flee from thy spirit?'

When pestilence struck the population of England again during the fifteenth century, ideas about combating it had not changed or made progress. There are at least three treatises dealing with it, written at different times and by different people, up to the reign of Henry VII. Not one of them has anything new to say and not one of them couples the recurring outbreaks with the neglect of the ordinary rules of hygiene. The first comes from the pen of John

Stipse, 'usinge surgerye within the Universytie of Oxforde, dwellings in the paryche of Est St Aldate, in fysshe strete at St Olldys churchestyle in the yere of our Lorde 1472'. The second was compiled by a Dominican: 'a trety that is nedeful and necessarie ayinst the pestilens... gadered and sette togidre on englissh [by] a master of divinitie of the ordre of frere prechoures Master Thomas Multon'. The third was written by Thomas Forestier in 1485 and dedicated to Henry VII. He was a native of Avranches and a member of the medical faculty there. All of these writers borrow extensively from John of Burgundy's tract composed one hundred years and more earlier. And even private practitioners, like Henry Horne, pretending to give personal advice in a letter addressed to Thomas Goldstone, Prior of Canterbury, couched their recommendations in identical words.

The fact is that medical science had become stereotyped and fixed. The education given to students was based on texts that had been traditional in the schools since the thirteenth century and, even though they had access to books produced by their contemporaries in the fourteenth and fifteenth centuries, these books merely repeated, without adding one iota to previously accumulated knowledge, the same threadbare theories and ideas. Even when they were confronted with such tragic occurrences as pestilences and plagues, they did not use their common sense and investigate the true cause, but explained it all away on purely theoretical, often fantastic, grounds.

Chapter Fourteen

Hospitals

The fundamental change in social conditions brought about by Christianity was most noticeable in its attitude towards the poor and suffering. This found expression in the institution of houses of hospitality where orphans, widows, the homeless, the old, and those who had no means of subsistence could find shelter. In these buildings, erected, sponsored and administered by people with ideals, the sick were the object of special attention. These institutions, at first private in origin, gradually came under the protection of the Church, and the bishops took over the responsibility for their upkeep, government and organisation. From the fourth century onwards an ever-growing concern with the foundation and development of such institutions can be seen in ecclesiastical legislation, and by the eighth century their definite medical character can be discerned in the obligation, imposed by the *liber diurnus*, of providing physicians to tend the sick who were lodged there.

In this work of public charity the Monastic Orders played a not inconspicuous part. Though the infirmarian in each abbey was appointed to deal exclusively with the sick of his own community, it was not long before his services were demanded by travellers, pilgrims and the people of the nearby countryside. In course of time, annexed to the other conventual buildings outside the cloister, there rose a secular infirmary in which the ailments of layfolk could be treated. As 'time progressed several religious Orders were founded, whose sole aim was the alleviation of sickness and suffering, and under their aegis many hospitals were built either in towns, or along the major roads, near dangerous rivers or in the mountain passes. By the fifteenth century they could be numbered in their thousands and in England alone there were seven hundred and fifty.

The hospital buildings were constructed at the outset on no definite plan and may have been ordinary dwelling houses adapted for this specific use. But when the monks began to construct infirmaries and hospitals as separate units within the complex of monastic buildings, a definite lay-out was conceived. At St Gall (although the plan may not have been put into execution) provision was made for separate wards for the seriously ill, and for those who had been let blood, for a pharmaceutical dispensary, for a bathroom, kitchen and lavatories and for staff rooms, all looking out on to a herb garden where the most common medicaments could be grown. The size of the rooms may be envisaged from those at Farfa where four out of six rooms, having two beds in each, measured about thirty by twenty-five feet. By the twelfth century the plan of a large hall with a chapel at the east end was widely adopted, particularly by the Cistercians; the beds were placed at right angles to the wall, usually under the windows, and ample space was allowed in the centre of the building for the movement of staff. The monastic infirmaries had room for eighty or even a hundred beds, but the smaller secular hospitals, which sometimes catered for no more than thirteen inmates, were necessarily built on a more modest scale. The finest remaining example in England of such a hospital is St Mary's, Chichester, now a great hall of four bays. A wide and lofty roof with open timbers spans the whole building, the pitch of the roof necessitating north and south walls that are unusually low. This open type of hospital gave more than adequate light and air to the sick, but it had the disadvantage of being cold in winter and difficult to heat. Later on, therefore, wooden or stone screens were erected to divide the hall into separate cubicles, and this system can be seen at Wells, Chichester and Norwich; the ruins of Rievaulx, Fountains and Furness show that the Cistercians also found this arrangement more suitable.

Sanitary arrangements varied according to the site and the size of the establishment, but they were always more than adequate.

The Cistercians followed a uniform plan. Their abbeys were built close to the banks of a river; about half a mile upstream they made a dam, diverted the water through channels that ran under all the monastic buildings – kitchens, lavatories, workshops and the various sections of the infirmary – and opened the sluices about half a mile down-stream, so that all the sewage and filth entered the river at a reasonable distance away. For hospitals in towns this method was not always feasible, but in a great many instances we find that they were erected in close proximity to running water into which pipes and drains carried all their refuse.

To provide themselves with good clean water both for drinking and washing purposes monasteries and other religious houses had constructed cisterns, laid down pipes, erected fountains in the cloister garth and employed several other useful and ingenious means. This was a costly business which only large communities, endowed with ample revenues and sufficient labour, could undertake. But quite early on it was accepted that wherever a group of people were gathered together under one roof, some kind of water system should be devised. The smaller hospitals therefore followed suit, earlier or later according to the means at their disposal, though their cisterns and pipes were not always made of lead, but of hollowed trunks of trees or stone.

Though we understand by hospitals places for the sick and infirm, this was not necessarily the interpretation placed upon the word in medieval times, and in most hospitals the sick lay side by side with the old and decrepit, and the poor who had no means of subsistence. There were, besides, those who were neither sick nor indigent, people who for personal motives preferred to end their days in a hospital where all their needs would be met, or who wished to remain there until such time as their personal problems had been resolved. Whatever their condition, they all received the same treatment.

It is unfortunate that few accounts survive from the hospitals in England. There are a number of copies of statutes determining the admission of brethren and sisters to minister to the sick; there are accounts of visitation with the results of enquiries into the running of these establishments; there are also a number of chartularies giving details of the lands, the sources of income and the extent of the buildings; but we lack completely the documents which could tell us about the day-to-day administration of the hospitals, about the treatment given to the sick, or about the general running of these institutions. Even for as important a place as St Bartholomew's hospital in London we possess no more than a list of charters recounting the various gifts that were made for the support of the hospital. Details of the medical treatment, of the heating, lighting, care of beds, sanitary arrangements and so on, have all disappeared. Such items must be gleaned from isolated instances, often from widely differing places and circumstances, and compounded together in order to give any composite picture of the medieval hospital and the manner in which it was run. In France the hospitals have been more fortunate and on the whole their records have been preserved more or less intact. It is for this reason that, on the assumption that most hospitals were administered on the same lines, we take our account of the day-to-day arrangements for the care of the sick from the archives of the Hôtel Dieu at Paris.

When a sick person presented himself at the hospital for admission, his clothes were taken from him and he was put to bed. His garments were then washed and put away in a safe place, together with any valuables he may have brought with him. The rooms or long halls in which the sick lay were kept spotlessly clean. Accounts for the hospital in Paris show that 1,300 brooms were used every year and that once a year, at Easter or thereabouts, all the walls were lime-washed. During winter a large fire was lighted in each hall, and to supplement it four large iron baskets filled with burning coals were moved up and down in the space between the two lines of beds that stood near the walls. In summer an ingenious system of pulleys with ropes enabled the patients to open and close the windows according to the level of the temperature, whilst the windows themselves were filled with coloured glass to regulate the bright rays and the heat of the sun. The number of beds in each hospital ward was regulated by the size of the building and the size of the beds; but it has been estimated that each bed was intended to hold at least two, and perhaps three, persons. This was the common usage of the time and was based on the kind of beds which could be found in any household, examples of which can be seen in miniature paintings of the period.

The beds consisted of a mattress filled with straw suspended on cords stretched between the four corner posts. The sick man, unclothed but with his head encircled by a piece of rolled linen, lay upon a pillow of feathers, and was covered with a counterpane that hung over both sides of the bed. These counterpanes were made from heavy grey cloth, sometimes bordered with white leather; other coverlets were made of fur from the skins of squirrels, foxes, rabbits, lambs, goats and other animals. Since they had to be kept free from vermin, furriers came to the hospital each year in the month of July; they pounded the fur, carded it, cleaned it and repaired any tears or holes, a task that usually took thirty men a month to perform. The cost of this was considerable. Nevertheless all the bedding was renewed three times a year, at the beginning of Lent, then at Whitsun and the beginning of November. Everyone took part in this labour, even the sick who were well enough to get about, and when all was over, a banquet was held at which fish, meat and other delicacies were eaten.

The use of linen sheets for the patients demanded a considerable laundry staff. At Paris there were between eight and nine hundred sheets to wash every week, not counting the garments of those patients newly admitted to the hospital. A permanent staff of fifteen laundresses was appointed to deal with this problem, the actual washing being done in the river that ran by the side of the hospital.

The daily round of the hospital staff began at five each morning, when, after rising and washing, they went downstairs to the church for matins. The sisters then went about their different employments, the laundry, the wards, the hall for admittance and so on. When the patients were awake, each sister went round a number of beds with a basin in one hand, a towel in the other, and washed the hands and faces of the sick. Later, whilst the beds were being made, the less sick patients were allowed to get up, the more seriously sick being moved to the vacant beds.

A manservant or orderly then proceeded to wash down the floor of the hall with water. There was a plentiful supply of water within the hospital itself, especially from the middle of the fourteenth century, and taps were placed at various convenient points in the building, not merely for ordinary uses, but also as a precaution in case of fire.

The provision of food was suitably well organised. Though a certain amount of bread was bought from local tradesmen, the hospital possessed its own bakery with a master baker, an assistant baker and two servants to make most of the bread consumed on the premises. The kitchen staff was larger. The master cook had three servants under him to prepare the vegetables, turn the spits, and scour the dishes, with an additional assistant to prepare and cook the tripe from sheep and pigs. Each week he went to the hospital's farm in the country to choose the animals he wished to have slaughtered, and every two days he was provided with a list of sick people whom he would have to provide with meat. He usually arranged to have fifty to eighty portions of meat from one sheep, according to its size. The basic meat food was mutton; beef was rarely served, as being too expensive; veal, lamb and pork were provided only on certain feast-days during the year, perhaps twelve times in all. But to this was added broth or soup, eggs, fish, fruit (such as raisins, apples and pears), cheese and sweets. As meat was provided only four times a week, herrings, fresh or salted, or other kinds of fish, were substituted.

Normally, there were two meals a day, one in the morning, the other in the evening. A bell sounded at eleven in the morning for the first meal, and at six in the evening for dinner or supper. Each patient had his own eating vessels, an earthenware pot to hold his ration of beer or wine, a drinking cup, a wooden platter and a wooden spoon.

Statutes for English hospitals reveal more or less the same picture. Meat was eaten only three times a week, sometimes salted, but mostly fresh. Cattle which had died of the murrain and which were often eaten by peasants and the poor in general were not allowed to be served to the patients. This was a wise precaution in view of the disease caused and aggravated by the consumption of inadequately salted meat and fish, bread made from blighted corn, and food contaminated in various ways. On the days when meat was not served, eggs, fish, cheese, butter, vegetables and salt were substituted. The usual allowance of drink was one gallon of beer, and of bread one loaf, the qualities of both sometimes being specified. There was also porridge and various types of gruel. On feast days it was usual to change this rather monotonous diet and then poultry (a goose between four patients!), salmon and other things were provided, often supplemented by generous gifts from benefactors.

The hygiene, heating and lighting of the English hospitals was also up to the French standard. Faggots were allocated to the patients according to the season of the year, whilst, as regards cleanliness, bath tubs were in use, women's heads were washed weekly, men's hair and beards were trimmed or shaved each week and their personal clothing washed at least twice a week by the laundresses attached to the hospital.

All in all the medieval hospital patient had little to complain about. Though the diet may have been unimaginative, the comfort of the patient was adequately provided for. The service of the sisters or brothers was always willing and attentive, inspired as it was by religious motives. There was always someone on duty, both day and night, and the sick had not the feeling that they were a nuisance or a burden. Even when they were cured of their infirmity they were not sent home straight away, but were kept in convalescence for another seven days to make sure there would be no relapse.

What kind of medical care was available for patients in these hospitals? It is generally assumed that since the hospitals were ecclesiastical institutions more attention was paid to the spiritual needs of the sick than was given to the purely medical aspects of the sickness; that it was a case of nursing rather than of curing. No doubt there is some basis for this belief, but it rests more on lack of evidence than on positive proof.

If we examine evidence from the Continent, where documents have been preserved, we find that both physicians and surgeons were attached to hospitals from the beginning of the thirteenth century. The oldest document of the Hôtel Dieu at Paris concerning the duties of the surgeon dates back to 1221, that to the services of a physician to 1231. Since the oldest statutes of the hospital only go back to 1117, it will be seen that the hospital began to organise its medical as distinct from its charitable care of patients at an early date. Before that, presumably, the patients were tended by clerics and their assistants who had studied medicine: gradually, through the influence of ecclesiastical legislation passed at the Council of the Lateran in 1215, the clerics were superseded and laymen were employed by the Master of the hospital to visit the patients. The charters which are extant show that in October 1221 the surgeon, Master Hubert, contracted with the Master to care for the sick free of charge and to attend to any of the hospital staff who might need his services. In return he received a house at the rent of forty shillings in which he and his wife, together with a widow named Orry, could live during their lifetime. At the same time, Vincent des Bois, a physician, contracted to give his services free to the sick of the hospital. And henceforward the tradition seems to have persisted that the hospital should have attached to its staff both qualified physicians and surgeons, among them being the celebrated Jean Pitard, surgeon to Philip le Bel and master of Henri de Mondeville. That this was not an isolated case can be proved by similar documents emanating from such diverse places as Argentan, Angers, Amiens, Dijon, Lyons, Nîmes, Grenoble and Saint Quentin. In the Low Countries such a contract is found at Bruges about 1280.

One of the most interesting sidelights on this question occurs in a description of the city of Milan, written about 1288 by Friar Bonvesin della Riva. He says:

In the city, including the suburbs . . . there are ten hospitals for the sick, all properly endowed with sufficient temporal resources. The principal one is the Hospital of the Brolo, very rich in possessions, and founded by Geoffrey de Bussero in 1145. In it, as its brethren testify, there are found, particularly in bad times, more than five hundred bed patients and as many more not lying down. All these receive food at the expense of the hospital itself. Besides them, there

M

are 350 babies or more, placed with individual nurses after their birth, under the hospital's care. Every kind of poor person, except lepers, for whom another hospital is reserved, is received there, and kindly and bountifully restored to health, bed as well as food being provided. Also, *all the poor needing surgical care are diligently cared for by three surgeons* who are assigned to this particular task: they receive their salary from the commune. In conclusion, no man in misery or want is refused or rejected. In the vicinity there are fifteen other hospitals, or thereabouts.

In another passage the Friar records that Milan had twenty-eight physicians and more than 150 surgeons 'of different specialities, a great many of whom, being excellent physicians, have learned from members of their family the ancient traditions of surgery'.

For England the evidence is not so strong. We know that at least two hospitals had the services of a qualified medical practitioner, namely the hospitals of St Nicholas, Carlisle, and St Leonard's, Derby. Both were under the mastership of Thomas de Goldington, who, in 1341, was acting as surgeon to the Scottish rebels and almost lost his appointment as a result of it, and who, in 1348, was exercising 'the office of surgeon to the Commonalty of Derby'. Official documents show that he was not an exemplary character and that he was reprimanded more than once for not observing the rules and constitutions of the houses he was supposed to supervise. But the complaints seem more concerned with the internal discipline of the hospitals rather than with his competent attendance on the sick. Besides him, an impressive list of Oxford graduates in medicine could be drawn up, who served as Wardens or Masters of hospitals. Among them occur such names as John Arundell, physician to Henry VI, Warden of Bethlehem; Nicholas Colnet, physician to the King, 1413–20, Warden of St Bartholomew's, Playden, Sussex; William Hobbes, physician to Edward IV, Warden of Bethlehem in 1479; John Malverne, physician to Henry IV, Master of St Katharine's, 1398–1409; John Middleton, physician to Richard II and Henry IV, Master of St Nicholas hospital, York, and Robert Sherborn, Warden of Holy Trinity, and at the same time Master of St Cross, Winchester. Many others could be added to this list.

But the question is: Did they exercise their profession as physicians and surgeons in the hospitals of which they had charge, or was their office a mere sinecure, bestowed on them by the King as a reward for personal services? It would appear that in a great number of instances their office was more honorary than onerous, and that their chief concern was the salary that accompanied the post rather than the medical care of the sick.

On the other hand, there are indications that professional medical attention was given to patients in hospitals. At Coventry the warden and master of the hospital was a man named Greenborough: his volume of medical works still survives and the marginal notes, the additions to remedies and other observations scattered throughout the pages appear to show that he was practising on his patients there. A volume of medical tracts belonging to the Dominican Friars at Warwick also survives, which shows by the progressive additions in the margins, especially in the treatises dealing with women's diseases, that they also gave professional medical attention to the sick. But we do not possess, as do the hospitals abroad, any series of contracts between physicians and hospitals which would provide us with convincing proof. Though there is no evidence for physicians and surgeons being *attached* to hospitals, it can be assumed, on the parallel evidence from the monasteries, that they were called in to give their assistance.

From the middle of the thirteenth century, after ecclesiastical legislation forbade the practice of medicine to monks and canons, it became the established tradition to have a physician or surgeon under some kind of tenuous, not necessarily written, contract to attend the sick in the monastic community when it was needed. Such an agreement was made between the Prior of Ely and John de Walford, physician, in 1278. In the succeeding years until the dissolution of the monasteries the Infirmarer's accounts of such abbeys as Abingdon, Gloucester, Oseney, Worcester, Norwich, and notably Westminster give ample details to prove that Physicians and surgeons were at their beck and call for an annual stipend. Some paid fees for particular cases, and it may be surmised that the same conditions prevailed in the administration of the hospitals.

In this connection the frequent assertion that the Church encouraged an exclusively spiritual approach to disease and set its face against the scientific pursuit of medicine should not go unchallenged. It is true that in the utterances of the saints we encounter expressions which strongly condemn the appeal to physical means for healing sickness. We hear Saint Bernard, for instance, reproaching his monks for seeking the aid of a doctor and pouring scorn on those who put their trust in Hippocrates and Galen. But this was not a condemnation of medicine as such. What Saint Bernard intended to convey was that patience, fortitude and a truly religious spirit are more effective in combating hypochondria, melancholy and self-pity than any recourse to pills, potions and other paraphernalia of the physician. It was one of the hazards of monastic life that the tedium produced by the monotonous round of daily duties brought in its train a morbid interest in health and its fluctuating vicissitudes. Saint Bernard himself has written a vivid description of the monk who is always going to the mirror to examine his complexion and his sunken cheeks. This morbidity, which was psychological in origin, was directly antagonistic to monastic discipline and could be counteracted only by psychological and spiritual means. Saint Bernard, who had passed through such trials himself, understood better than most that it was the mind, and not the body, which needed healing. His strictures, therefore, on doctors and medical remedies should be read in this light. As has been seen, when it was a question of a real, physical infirmity or disease, the doctor was invariably called in.

A few words should be added here about the treatment of psychological cases, especially of those where an act of crime had been committed and the question of diminished responsibility arose. The general assumption seems to be that the Middle Ages was far more brutal in these matters than we are today and that mental patients were bound with thongs, flogged, put into irons, thrown into noisome prisons and dungeons or even executed as felons. It may come as a surprise to learn that this was by no means the case. The law in England, at least from the thirteenth century onwards, was not very different from what it is today, and the treatment meted out to offenders was mild, reasonable and compassionate. Fortunately, there are a number of definite cases which provide evidence to establish this point, and the following are a few of them.

In 1270 a court was held at Norwich gaol to try Richard Blofot of Cheddestan for the murder of his wife and children. The jurors said that as Richard and his wife were returning from Rapham market they passed by a marlpit full of water. Richard, seized with a sudden frenzy, threw himself into it and tried to drown himself and was saved only by his wife dragging him out. Eventually they reached home and since Richard appeared to have calmed down and was behaving himself quietly, his wife left the house to get some necessities. Whilst she was out Richard's frenzy erupted once more and he killed his two children. When the wife returned and found the two children dead, she broke out into cries of grief, which so enraged him that he attacked and killed her. The noise aroused the neighbours, who ran to the house to discover what was afoot, and when they got in they found Richard trying to hang himself.

At the trial Richard pleaded not guilty, and the court, considering all the circumstances, came to the conclusion that he was not fully responsible. He was therefore put into prison. Six years later the King sent a commission to John Lovetoft to enquire whether Richard could be safely released or not, and the reply was that though he was at that time sufficiently sensible and behaved reasonably, it could not be said that he was so far restored as to be set free without danger to himself, especially in the heat of summer.

In 1285 an inquisition was held at Beverley as the result of a writ sent by the king to the sheriff of York. It appeared that on the Wednesday after the feast of Saint Wilfrid (17 October, 1285) Brother Walter of the hospital was lying in his chamber after dinner. Richard the clerk, to whom he was deeply attached, was lying sick in the same chamber, and had been carefully tended by Walter during the whole of his long illness. One day, 'rendered frantic and mad by his sickness', he suddenly rose from his bed and 'smote brother Walter as he slept, first with a bench and afterwards with a trestle, so that all his brains came out'. Immediately after doing this Richard went out into the courtyard and kitchen with his hands still covered with brains and blood. And when the other brethren asked him what he had done, he laughed and said: 'I have killed my dear master, brother Walter. Come and see where he lies slain. He will never speak another word.' And he brought them to the slain man, saying: 'Did I not say truthfully that he was slain?' At the trial he was convicted of killing by misadventure during a fit of madness: 'and so being mad, he was taken and imprisoned, and still persists in his madness'.

A slightly different case came before the King in 1358, when a son was accused of attacking his father with a sword and grievously wounding him. At the enquiry it was found that the father, 'led by an evil spirit', often upbraided the boy and provoked quarrels. The son, enraged by this continuous persecution, finally took up a sword and wounded him. The question of guilt, therefore, turned on whether the son had done it out of malice, whether he was *compos mentis*, or whether, on the other hand, the father was to blame. The jury arrived at the conclusion that the son was not guilty of any felony or crime and acquitted him. The father however was judged to be a psychological case and consequently not responsible for his actions. Many other examples of the same kind could be adduced to show that people in the Middle Ages were far more lenient to mentally unbalanced people than their successors of the eighteenth century. The tradition of humane treatment and a realistic appraisal of mental disease is apparent even in the Romances, and one of the Arthurian legends which recounts the story of Lancelot's madness shows the practical way in which such cases were dealt with. Insanity was considered to be curable through physical and mental methods without any recourse to demonology, especially in psychoses which had been caused through emotional upset. In the play *Le Jeu de la Feuillée* the madman is presented with vivid realism, a paranoiac with delusions of grandeur, with a persecution complex and haunted by fears that people plan to murder him. He is destructive, restless, noisy, indecent and sexually uninhibited, insulting to his father and threatening to kill him. The play introduces an ecclesiastic who attempts to cure the madness by using holy relics. But the common-sense attitude of the normal person is shown by the fact that this attempt is shown to fail, and that the final treatment to be recommended is quiet and rest at home. One of the first hospitals to be devoted exclusively to the care of mental patients was the colony established at Gheel in Belgium during the thirteenth century. The colony was centred round the shrine of Saint Dympna, the daughter of a pagan Irish chieftain, who fled from her country to escape an incestuous marriage. Her father, in a fit of insane rage, murdered her together with the priest who had advised her, and she thus became the patron saint of those afflicted with mental maladies. Where she died a church and an infirmary were erected and patients were brought there from far and wide to be cured. Those who remained at the shrine were boarded out with peasants in the neighbourhood, whilst retarded children were given work to do in the fields. In this way a new system for treating defectives was evolved and is in active existence to this day.

In England there was no comparable institution until the fourteenth century when an attempt was made by a chaplain, Robert Denton, to found a hospital in All Hallows, Barking, for priests and others 'who suddenly fell into a frenzy and lost their memories'. This particular attempt failed through lack of funds and the property assigned for the foundation was eventually given to St Katharine's Hospital near the Tower. But there was another hospital outside Bishopsgate, called St Mary Bethlem, which had been established since 1247 and which was converted for this purpose about the close of the fourteenth century. Originally it had served as a hospice for the Bishop of Bethlehem on his visits to this country and the brethren and sisters there had begged money for the use of the church in the Holy Land. In course of time it was taken from the Bishop and put under the protection of the City of London. In 1403, when there was an outcry about the misapplication of funds, a visitation was made on orders from the King, and it was at this juncture that the fact emerged that Bethlem was treating mental patients. In the report made on the state of the hospital it was disclosed that six men, out of the total number of fourteen inmates, were *mente capti*, that is, out of their senses. Furthermore, it transpired from the inventory of goods found in the hospital that some iron fetters, manacles and stocks, that had been used in the place previously, were missing and they had been misappropriated or sold by the janitor, who was the main culprit in the embezzlement of funds. A further accusation against him was that 'the aforesaid Peter takes no trouble to keep within the bounds of the said hospital the men and women of unbalanced mind, and the sick, unless he is paid a certain sum of money each week'.

The mention of fetters, irons and stocks has led some commentators to conclude that the treatment of unbalanced patients inside the hospital was of the crude and brutal kind: they fail to take notice of the reference to their being allowed to wander at will outside the precincts of the hospital. There is no doubt that some patients were placed under restraint when they were violent, a practice that had been counselled by the most enlightened physicians in classical times, but these periods would be of short duration and such instruments would be dispensed with as soon as the paroxysms had worn off. It is unfortunate that all the documents relating to this hospital prior to the Reformation have disappeared, so that it is impossible to envisage what kind of treatment was meted out to patients. But the fact that some physicians, among them John Arundell, chaplain and physician to Henry VI, were appointed as wardens of the hospital may point to a desire to provide whatever medical and scientific means were available at that time for the benefit of the insane. William Gregory, Lord Mayor of London, who made a bequest in his will of forty shillings for the inmates, wrote: 'A church of Our Lady that is called Bedlam. And in that place are found many men that have fallen out of their wits. Right well are they cared for in that place, and some are restored to health again, but some are there for ever, for they are incurable.' That the house had a good reputation can be inferred from the distinguished men who held office there, such as William Hobbes, surgeon to Edward IV, Thomas Maudesley, one-time proctor of Cambridge University and chaplain to the mother of Henry VII; and by the fact that Henry VII himself maintained there at his own cost of six shillings and eightpence a quarter, one of his former esquires 'Raynesford, that is mad'. At the beginning of the sixteenth century a confraternity was formed for the purpose of attracting more alms to the place. In the certificate that was issued to all those who gave donations it was stated that the house, and the Order to which it belonged, had done great services for 'the mentally afflicted, the insane, the frenzied and others, who with great care and diligence are frequently cured by the unceasing attention of physicians'. What success the confraternity had, we have no means of knowing. But it is obvious that up to the time of the Dissolution the hospital was functioning properly. Sir Thomas More, who lived in Bishopsgate from 1516 to 1523, recalled that 'in Bedlam thou shalt see one laughing and the knocking of his head against a post, and yet there is little pleasure therein': and later, about 1533, he mentioned a man who used to behave improperly towards women in church and 'who had been put in Bedlam, and afterwards by beating and correction gathered his remembrances to come again to himself'.

On the whole it would seem that the attitude towards unbalanced people was kindly and tolerant, full of compassion rather than of criticism, based on the realisation that mental disturbance was often the outcome of emotional upset and resulted in diminished responsibility. It was to be a long time before this attitude returned, for the later history of Bethlem shows how callous the public could become.

Chapter Fifteen
Vernacular Texts

During the late fourteenth century and early fifteenth a new phenomenon appeared in England. This was the writing of treatises in English. Up to that time all books, whether on philosophy, theology, law, literature, medicine or other sciences, had been written in Latin or French. In the schools, except at the Universities where Latin was prescribed, children construed their lessons in French, whilst among the nobility and gentry French was the language for polite conversation. But almost contemporary with the appearance of Chaucer's *Canterbury Tales* a flood of literature written in English swamped the older texts. Trevisa, in his translation of Higden's *Polychronicon*, dates this change from the time of the Black Death, for he says that since 'the first Moreyn this manner [of using French] was som del ychaungide'. The teaching of English in the schools is attributed to a certain schoolmaster named Master Cornwall and his example was so eagerly followed that by 1385, when Trevisa was writing, it had become general. Among the fields of knowledge which benefited by this revolution in methods of education, medicine profited to an enormous extent. Whereas previously the use of English had been limited to the insertion of medical recipes into the margins of books, now whole treatises, written by laymen for laymen, began to pour from the shops of the stationers. Many of these were in verse to assist the reader to consign them to memory. They covered every topic concerning health and disease: bloodletting, uroscopy, herbal lore, regimen for health, prognostications of disease, and surgery.

But side by side with them, written in prose, went complete treatises of a more scientific nature, suitable for professional medical men.

Most of these were not original works, but translations of standard texts used by physicians and surgeons during previous centuries. One of the earliest of these texts was the *Liber Floridus* attributed to Macer, which dealt with the pharmaceutical powers of certain herbs. It was translated into English by a schoolmaster, John Love by name. 'Macer made a boke in latyn. The whiche boke Johannes Lelamour scolemaster of Herforde Est, they he unworthy was, in the yere of oure Lord anno MCCC lxxiii tornyd into ynglis.' What is interesting, apart from the fact that a text of it belonged to Richard Dod, barber surgeon of London, is that the manuscript containing this treatise had other tracts on gynaecology and astrology and Galen's *De sectis*, in English, Latin and French. Other treatises on specific herbs were translated about the same time. One on the virtues of rosemary, which had wide circulation, was translated by Friar Henry Daniel, a Dominican: 'These ben the sum of the vertues of Rosemary, as the clerke of Salerne seyde and wrote to the Cowntes of Hynde (Hainault) and sche sende hem to here doughter Phylype that was weddyd to the kyng of Engelond.' Henry Daniel appears to have specialised in this kind of work, for he also translated the work of Isaac Judaeus on urines, which he dedicated to his friend Walter Ketton, a professional physician, in 1377, under the title of *The Dome of Urines*. Lay-folk naturally were more concerned with the day-to-day remedies which they could apply to more common ailments. A great number of treatises were drawn up for their convenience, mostly compilations from accepted authorities, but there were also books of remedies which had been tried and tested by lords and ladies, parish priests, friars and canons. A typical example is the *Liber de Diversis Medicinis*, which contains the usual doctrine of the established medical texts together with remedies recommended by the parish priest of Oswaldskirk in Yorkshire. Another text (Sloane 1313) gives recipes from John Jonys, Doctor Robinson, Cardinal John (of Toledo), Doctor Hare, William Davers, Gowre, wife of Porter, William Davies, from the wife of John Harell, Joan Molleville, and

a certain knight named West, who was a member of the Order of
St John. Books that had been written for people in high places
carried with them an authority of their own, and so we find
numerous translations of the regimen drawn up for Queen Isabel,
wife of Edward II: 'This was written from Montpileris to Quene
Isabel of Ynglonde at ye preier of ye kyng of Fraunce hir brother.'
This tract deals mostly with foods, giving advice on their effects,
both good and bad, on various members of the body. One of the
most popular treatises that survives in many copies is the systematic handbook dealing with every disease from head to foot: 'Here
begynneth gode medycyns for al manner yvellis that every man
hath that gode lechys have drawen owt off ye bokys that men clepe
Archipuus and Ypocras ffor thies ware ye best lechis off the world in
here tyme and therfor who so will do as thys boke wyll tech hyme
he may be sekyr to have help off all evellys and woundys and other
desesys and sekeness both within and eke withowt.' Quite a number
of these texts were drawn up by Friars, particularly the Dominicans, who were in constant contact with the poor. The manuscript,
Sloane 3498, is attributed to 'Frere Randolf', sometimes called elsewhere 'Frere Roland'. It begins: 'Brother, I praye the for charite
that thou write to me a fewe medecynes that I myght helpe pore
folk that falleth into sekenes and beth unkonnyng to helpe hem
sylfen and of unpower to hyre hem leches.' This text is in dialogue
form, dealing systematically with the principles of medicine, the
temperaments, humours, kinds of medicine, and even various
weights and measures. 'Brother, leches have a queynt maner writ-
yng and hard for to rede in makyng of hir medicynes'; so he
explains in simple language the meaning of the formulas *R, ana,
lib., di., m.s.* and so on. These texts were not mere folk medicine,
but based on old authors: 'Here beginneth the tretees of Phisik
that Frere Randolf made and drewe oute of diverse bokes, the best
that he coude finde within Engelond.' The same manuscript contains a pestilence tract for poor people: 'Here beginnes a tretys that
is nedefull and necessarie ayenst the pestilens that nowe is regnand,
the wich trety gaddered and sette togedre on Englissh a master of
diviniti of the Ordre of Frere prechours, Master Thomas Multon,
of divers doctours of Phisik where thei treted of the mater of

pestilens.' After stating the four reasons why he made this compilation, the friar said: 'And these iiii causes meves me to gader this trety and sette it on Englissh that every man both lerned and lewed may the better understand hit and do thereafter, And to be his owne phisicien in tyme of nede ayenst the venym and the malice of the pestilence.'

An indication of the widespread interest in health and disease, apart from the diffusion of purely medical texts, is found in the translations, abridgements and incorporation into purely literary texts of the *Secretum secretorum* supposedly written by Aristotle for Alexander the Great. This treatise, for which no Greek original exists, goes back to the eighth century, when a Syriac version was translated into Arabic by Jahja Ibn al-Batrik. A Latin version was made by John of Spain sometime between 1128–30 and it enjoyed unprecedented success: it was known and quoted by Michael Scot, Albert the Great, Thomas Aquinas and Roger Bacon, and quite early it inspired works of a similar nature, such as the *De administratione principum* of Gerald of Wales. The earliest mention of it in English vernacular literature occurs in Chaucer where it is attributed to Arnold of Newe Toun (that is Arnold of Villanova, who wrote a commentary on it). About 1390 Gower based Book Seven of his *Confessio Amantis* on it, Thomas Occleve made a translation about 1412, *The Regement of Princes,* and then in quick succession appeared three prose versions, *The Governance of Lordschippes,* the *Secrete of Secretes,* and the *Governaunce of Prynces* by James Yonge (1422). Other versions followed, first by Chaucer's pupil, John Lydgate, monk of Bury (1370–1451), then by Benedict Burgh, Lydgate's pupil, next by John Shirley, and afterwards by several others.

The text of the *Secrete of Secretes* opens by expounding the qualities and duties of a king, but it soon passes on to discussing medical topics, such as 'Of keeping of helthe; Of governance of seeknes: in how many maners a man may kepe helthe; Of dyvers metis; Of the stomak; Signes to knowe the stomak; Of abstenance; Nought to drynke pure watir, and The maner for to slepe.' The four parts of the body, their ailments and their appropriate remedies are dealt with briefly and, after a short section on astronomy and physiognomy, the reader is advised not to trust in any one doctor. All these matters are dealt with, sometimes at greater length in other works, but what it proves is that they were well known, currently learned and discussed, and that, in some degree, they summarised the science of the day in popular form: for within sixty-five years of the appearance of the *Canterbury Tales* no fewer than eight literary works were derived in whole or in part from the original.

Besides the unlearned, and the poor and the rich amateur, there was another class of person for whom these vernacular tracts were useful, the non-professionally-trained practitioner, the village leech. In Harley MSS 1735 we have a typical collection of medical tracts on diet, urines, days for favourable treatment, miscellaneous receipts and poems, which form a reasonably complete handbook for diagnosis, treatment and prognosis. This belonged to John Crophill, a village practitioner of Wix, near Harwich. One page is headed: 'Here [be] the men and women that I, John Crophill of Wykys, hath scen hare uryn and don curys unto hem and med-synnys thoro the grace of god and houre lady & the holy gost.' Some 150 names from forty-six villages and towns in north-east Essex and south Suffolk are listed. Some of his patients lived as far away as Holton about fifty miles by road from Wix, showing that his reputation must have been widely known. Against the names is entered the fee paid to Crophill for his services, and these fees, though not comparable with those paid to professional physicians, are sufficiently high to indicate that he made a comfortable living from his practice. At Otley, for instance, he received from Richard Armigard five shillings and eight pence, from John Armigard seventeen pence halfpenny, from William Marriot twenty pence; in all, eight shillings and nine pence halfpenny, a considerable sum if all these patients were treated on the same day. On the other hand, he had his bad debtors: John Amys owed him six shillings and eight pence, plus a further twenty pence. In a note Crophill says: 'I had but four shillings and eight pence.'

The level of his medical treatment is illustrated by:

An ontment ffor gowte
Take the galle of an ox & a pece of a fat capon & meng hem to-
geder, & anoint the ther-with al, & the goute schal breke no iont of
no manere of wyse. . . .

This same receipt appears in other works and seems to be French in origin. Another example for the disease appears in a poem on Rosemary, a rhymed version of the tract written for the Countess of Hainault, and very popular:

> *If a man be bawllyn in qwhat place it be*
> *Of swellyng or gout or hoder prevete,*
> *Take rosemary & blak wolle & make a platour*
> *and bolle it in welle water & loke that it be cler,*
> *and let it on the bollyng, tho it be never so gret,*
> *All the venym is in, it hym don hout swet.*

There were probably hundreds of practitioners like Crophill in different parts of England and many of the similar collections of medical tracts may have belonged to them. Unfortunately, though many bear names of owners, none of them contains detailed notes comparable to those of the Crophill manuscript.

Apart from the vernacular texts which may have served the ordinary layman, there were others which were made for the use of professional physicians. Among these texts we find versions of Grafeus Benvenuti on eye diseases, of Gerard of Cremona, Platearius, Hippocrates, Galen, and a whole host of others. But the most surprising of all were the translations of surgical works: these covered practically every known medieval author, Roger Frugardi, Theodoric of Cervia, Bruno Longoburgo, William of Salicet, Lanfranc of Milan, Henri de Mondeville and Guy de Chauliac. At the same time we find compilations written in English based on the works of all these writers. This should not give rise to the misconception that the surgeons were unable to understand the original Latin texts and were, as the common idea runs, illiterate men. Many of these translations contain within the same covers other works written not only in Latin but also in French: a proof that their readers were capable of gaining instruction in more than one language, a capability denied to many surgeons of modern times. That these texts were used is shown by the annotations in the margins, by their being bequeathed in wills to apprentices and by their being passed from hand to hand by purchase. One such surgical text is known to have passed through the hands of four royal surgeons: John Jonson, surgeon to Elizabeth, wife of Henry VII; then to John Franke, surgeon to Henry VIII; then to John Ayliffe, also surgeon to Henry VIII, and finally to William Clowes, surgeon to the Earl of Sussex and Elizabeth I.

One of the earliest of the vernacular compilations on surgery may have been written as early as 1398. The author evidently had access to a rich library, for he quotes Hippocrates, Haly Abbas, Albucasis, Avicenna, Roger of Parma, the Four Masters, Averroes, Hugh of Lucca, Theodoric, Lanfranc and de Mondeville. Of most of these authors there were no English translations available at that time, so the compilation was made from the Latin texts. The compiler was not content with mere borrowing: he recorded his own experiences and his own investigations. For instance, in speaking of the anatomy of the head, where Mondeville had said that it contained four bones, whilst Avicenna said six, he remarked:

'But truly I have goon to all the gretteste charnellis that beth aboute London where that bethe scolle bonys withoute nombre for to proven by experience the veri sothe, and have handlid, seen and asserchid every boon of the heed by him silf. Wherefore y seie aftir that I saugh, and felde that by myn undirstdonynge ther beth sixe principal bonys of the heed which ben necessarie to the closynge and to the defense of the brayn.' And he goes on to say that all heads are not the same, for 'truly I foond in ye charnel of Seynt Marie spetil at Londoun a scolle boon that was al oon hool boon lyke a basenett. . . .'

There are several other illuminating passages of this nature indicating that the writer was a man of education, of critical judgment and of independent outlook.

Brother Roland who wrote a book of physic for the poor also wrote a treatise on surgery. He described various kinds of wounds and hurts caused by arrows, spears, swords and heavy staffs, and gave the methods by which they could be treated:

Brother, what and the schulle be to broken, how schal such a wound be heled, yf ther be a pece rent away of the sculle? May men sowdened ageyn as it was, rather outher sowden a pece of mater, outher of some other thyng in his stede to cover the brayne?

The answer to this and other questions suggests that the Friars were accustomed to use surgical instruments to cut open wounds, sew them together, and luxate fractures. But when it was a case of internal surgery, they did not operate:

But yf the hert be wounded, outher the lyver, outher the lyghts, outher the longes, outher the stomack, outher the mydryf, outher the reynes, outher the throttebolle, ne medle thou nought of hem.

This was the common attitude of the times, and it may be that this vernacular tract is but a compilation from the earlier work of Roland of Parma.

Another compilation of this period, which begins: 'Galyene that was lanterne of Fysiciens and surgens' has been attributed to Roger Marshall, Fellow of Peterhouse, Cambridge, from 1437–1460. Marshall was associated with William Hattecliffe and Dominic de Serego, both royal physicians, and with them was appointed to examine Joan Nightingale for symptoms of leprosy. He possessed an extensive library, most of which he bequeathed at his death to Peterhouse and to Gonville Hall, Cambridge. He is an obvious candidate for the authorship of this surgical work, but unfortunately at least one copy antedates his period. What is interesting about this compilation, as distinct from the earlier one of 1398, is that it makes extensive use of Guy de Chauliac, and in fact translates whole passages word for word. But it contains nothing personal. The parts, and they are numerous, which are translated from Mondeville, differ from corresponding passages in the 1398 compilation, and this shows that a number of people were making independent versions of Latin texts at this period.

Perhaps the most interesting book of surgery written in the vernacular during this time was the *Book of Fayre Surgery* compiled by Thomas Morstede. Morstede was perhaps the most eminent surgeon during the fifteenth century. In 1415, when the King was preparing to invade France, he was charged with the organisation of a surgical unit to look after wounded men: he chose twelve surgeons to accompany him and arranged for transport of the medical supplies during the campaign. When the second expedition set out for France in the following year he was granted powers to impress as many surgeons as he needed and to provide artificers who could make and repair surgical instruments. It was during these campaigns that he gained all his experience. Some years later, in 1423, he was appointed supervisor of the craft of surgery in the City of London and together with another eminent surgeon, William Bradwardyne, was sworn in as Master of the gild. By 1426 he had been made a Sheriff of the City and from that time onwards honours were showered upon him: he moved in court circles, became a member of the upper classes and died a rich man. Some time about 1446 he wrote his treatise on surgery, based primarily on the previous works of Henri de Mondeville and Guy de Chauliac, but containing also the fruits of his long experience on the battlefield: 'Wherefor to ye worschippe of al myghty gode and his glorios modyr Saynt Mary and all halows and to ye prophete (profit) of all crysten pepull and of studyars, practyzars in surgery, I have compyld and made this boke in ye yere of owre Lord MCCCC and xlvi.'

The book begins with fifteen chapters on anatomy after which come twenty-five chapters on different hurts and wounds; these are followed by sixty-two chapters on various other diseases, ending with morphew, and the work ends with a list of remedies and unguents. Some of these remedies are taken from John Arderne, others from Master Fyncham (not otherwise known). In speaking of anatomy he remarks that knowledge of it can be gained in two ways, either by books or by observation: 'For ye parts of ye membres may better be sene with eyne in ded, than in letters wretyne on ye boke ... for lechys may be experte throw syght of newly dede mannys bodys as them whos heddys have be smetyne of, or hangunge, be ye wyche may be made anathomie of membyrs.' He then describes the procedure for dissection: 'and pryncipally in this wyse do ye body be layd on a bank, the on parte of the body upward and ye nether parte downwarde, and do make therof iiii lessiones after whan ye body ys opyn and every holowe parte longynge therto.' We must not hastily infer from this passage that Morstede had practised dissection or that in England, at this period, dissection for anatomical purposes was taught. The passage above is a mere translation from Guy de Chauliac and can be paralleled in other vernacular translations.

But another passage of far more importance is the following:

And yt ys to understond that in ye yer of owr Lord MCCCCmo and iii in ye iiiith yer of Kynge Henry ye iiiith on Mary Maudelen Evyn at ye batell of Shrewesbery, yt happen soo that Henry ye worthy prynce and eyr of ye sayd Henry kynge was smetyn in ye face besyd ye nose on ye lefte syd with an arow ye wyche sayd arow entryd over-wharte, and after ye shafte wase takyn owt and ye hede thereof abod styll in ye hyndyr parte of a bone of ye hede of ye mesur of vi ynche; and than was [called] JOHN BRADMOR surgan to ye kynge and helyd hym in ye castell of Kelyngsworth. To ye sayd castell came yat tyme dyverse wyse lechys sayand that thei wolde drawe owt ye arrowe hed with drynkys and odyr cures, but thei myghte note, and at the laste the sayd John Bradmore entryrmetynge of ye sayd cure and had owt ye arow hede wyth swyche an instrument, ye wyche instrument was mad in the maner of tonges and was rownde and holowysche, and be the mydds therof entryd a lytyll wyse, with ye wyche instrument was pullyd owt ye arrow hed, and afterward ye wounde was wasched in wyne and clensyd with mundificatyve onyment of iii parts of populion and ye iiiith part of hony, so continewynge ye space of vii dayes and afterward ye place was [helyd] with unguentum fuscum cirurgicum.

On the page where this operation is described there is an illustration of the instrument used by Bradmore.

This reference to the designing of special surgical instruments for complex operations draws attention to a detail not hitherto remarked upon. Most surgeons, besides being expert in medicine, were also skilled craftsmen in metal. Quite a number of them were silversmiths and goldsmiths and for that reason the official records mention their names in connection either with the minting of money or with the searching of vessels in the port of London to prevent coin of the realm from being exported. Thomas of Weseham, a royal surgeon, was one of the earliest moneyers of this type: Morstede was a member of the goldsmiths' gild, and both

John Bradmore and his relative, Nicholas, were arrested at one point on the charge of coining false money. It points to a wider type of education and culture among the surgeons than is to be found among the physicians of the period and makes the observation of Chaucer on the barber-surgeons more credible:

> *Wel koude he laten blood and clippe and shave*
> *And maken a chartre of lond or acquitance.*

So they were not ignoramuses, but quite capable of drawing up and writing legal documents, besides having a knowledge of medicine.

It would be impossible to discuss all the vernacular medical texts which proliferated at this period; they are too numerous, too diverse. But all point to a growing awareness among the general population that medicine, like other things, was becoming part of a liberal education and that a knowledge of it was not the exclusive property of professional physicians. In 1421 the physicians had endeavoured to have a bill passed which would have prevented any but university-trained men from meddling in the practice of medicine, and this indicated that they were already becoming powerless to prevent, not merely ordinary men, but women also, from encroaching on their domain. But, considering how few the professionals were and how great was the need for widespread medical attention, the authorities evidently thought legislation would be futile, and as a result no Act was passed. The production of vernacular texts continued unimpeded, people of all walks of life pursued their reading and use of medical texts, and even royal personages did not disdain to dabble in concocting remedies even when they had professional physicians at their side. Henry VIII, surrounded by no less than six physicians and surgeons, competed with his medical advisers in trying to cure himself, and a manuscript in the British Museum (Sloane 1047) contains not merely 'plasters devised by the King' at Greenwich, Westminster, St James and other places, but a series of ointments 'to coole and drye and comforte the membre' and a list of waters, lotions and decoctions. This was a tradition that was to persist. Even in the middle of the sixteenth century a text was being circulated, the purpose of which was to assist the layman to treat his own ailments and diseases: This booke of Sovereigne medicines against the most common of knowne diseases, both of men and women, was by good proofe, and longe experience collected by Mr Doctor Fecknam, late Abbot of Westmynster, that chieflie for the poore, which hath not att all tymes the Learned Phisitions att hande.'

Whether women took any part in these translations is not a question that can be answered with certainty. Women had been known to enter the profession of medicine, not merely as midwives, but as practising physicians. In Italy this was far from common, whereas in France it was frowned upon and in one instance led to a prolonged legal battle in which the University authorities were severely mauled. In 1306 Pierre Dubois addressed a letter to Edward I proposing that clever and attractive women should be educated as medical missionaries and sent to the East to help in the recovery of the Holy Land. He said:

> Let maidens be instructed in medicine and surgery along with the preliminary training necessary for these studies, so that when desirable they may be given in marriage to the higher princes, clerks and other wealthier men of the East. It cannot fail to come about that these women nobler and richer than other matrons, enjoying a reputation everywhere in medicine and surgery and such experiments as can be known, would have a strong attraction for those women who need their advice. . . .

This proposal was probably considered too daring and nothing came of it, but the scheme is a striking testimony to the medical ministrations of women at that time. It also points to the probability that the vernacular texts dealing with gynaecology, written expressly for women so that they need not have recourse to male practitioners, may have been written or translated by them.

Chapter Sixteen
The Final Phase

The century or more that elapsed between the introduction of English as a vehicle for medical writings and the foundation of the College of Physicians showed no significant advance in medical knowledge. The physicians, who were the product of the universities, continued to study, teach and comment upon the same texts that had been used in previous centuries, so that their works, and they were few, were merely pale reflections of what had been composed long before. Gaddesden, at the beginning of the fourteenth century, had synthesised all the ideas of writers previous to his time, borrowing from the Greeks, Arabs, Salernitans and a few of his contemporaries. And there, it seemed, English medicine was allowed to rest. The texts of several new continental writers filtered into the libraries of the more wealthy medical practitioners to take their place beside the works of Gilbert, Avicenna, Gordon and other veteran authorities, but the interest they aroused, judging by the few copies that survive, was negligible. Medicine, as a subject of research, took second place, even among physicians, to other scientific pursuits and appeared to be considered merely as a stepping-stone to higher dignities and social advancement.

A typical instance of this is Simon Bredon, Fellow of Merton College, Oxford, a physician celebrated enough to be called in to treat Johanna, Queen of Scots, when she fell ill at Hertford in 1358. Though he wrote at least fourteen works, only one is concerned with medicine, the rest dealing with astronomy, mathematics, trigonometry and astrology. His library, which was most extensive and contained practically all the well-known medical texts, shows that his interests were not confined to medicine, but covered law, astronomy, literature and other things. He had evidently spent much of his time in drawing up indexes to Avicenna, Averroes, Rhases, Mesue, Serapion, Platearius, Macer, the *Antidotarium* of Nicholas and the *Rogerina*, for in his will he stipulated that they should be copied out again by his clerk, Robert Valeys, according to instructions already given orally, and presented to Merton College. No activity more sterile than this can be imagined, for it adds not one iota to ideas previously available and merely encourages laziness in those who use them: it ensures that students will not read through these authors systematically, but simply use the indexes to find isolated ideas. It may be that Bredon made these indexes for his own use to facilitate the composition of his ambitious but futile work called *Trifolium*. The *Trifolium* as it exists today fills 120 manuscript leaves, yet in spite of its length it contains less than one-twelfth of the book as originally planned. Bredon's idea had been to devote one *Folium* to a discussion of health, a second to disease and a third to prophylactics. Each of these *Folia* was to be subdivided into a number of sections, each section being divided into several treatises, each containing a number of chapters. It was, in short, an imitation of Avicenna's *Canon*, but without any reference to surgery. The portion of this vast encyclopedia that survives today deals with the prognostication of disease based on all the substances that are evacuated from the body, such as urine, faeces, sweat, mucus and so on. It should have been followed by a tract on prognostications from the pulse and breathing, but in fact a large section on medicines has been interpolated, describing their composition, operation, effects, names, method of preparation and much else. The work is methodically and painstakingly carried out to the smallest detail, but is so derivative, so excruciatingly dull and devoid of interest that one can understand why it never attracted the attention of students or scholars. Bredon, nevertheless, enjoyed a high reputation in his time as a physician and the size of his library, his treasures of plate, his astrolabes and his undoubted wealth probably reflect the high fees he received for his services. He was, besides, a priest, holder of several benefices and warden of the hospital at Maidstone, so that whatever we may think of his achievements, his contemporaries held him in high esteem.

Another writer living about the same time was John Mirfield. His reputation rests not on any original contribution to the science of medicine but on his connection with the hospital of St Bartholomew. He was not, as has been asserted, a canon of the Augustinian Priory of St Bartholomew, but a secular priest who resided within its precincts. He was ordained in 1395 and died in 1407.

It has been said that he was trained by a skilled London surgeon, but the passage in his writings on which this statement is based happens to be an extract from the *Chirurgia magna* of Lanfranc of Milan, and it refers not to Mirfield's master or to a canon of London, but to Lanfranc and a canon of Milan. It is doubtful whether he ever practised medicine, for most of the references to actual cases which he describes are taken verbatim from other authors. It would seem that Mirfield's interest in medicine was mostly academic and that his compilation, the *Breviarium Bartholomaei*, was made not for his own use but for the benefit of those who could not afford books or wished to treat themselves. He confesses openly that he had not studied medicine professionally: 'Someone will perhaps ask me, why do you write what you have never properly studied under the eyes of a master?' He replies that his intention was to extract passages from previous authors to assist simple people like himself. But he had also another end in view: 'It has often happened that both in my own case and that of my friends I have experienced the frauds perpetrated by modern physicians ... And so I collected these remedies from various sources in order to avoid imposters wherever I should be and know how to treat both myself and Christ's poor when illness befell us.' Even this passage is copied from Pseudo-Pliny.

The *Breviarium Bartholomaei* is an enormous treatise covering every possible infirmity from head to foot. It is divided into fifteen books, each part being subdivided into several 'distinctions', which are again divided into chapters. It contains nothing original but consists solely of extracts from earlier authors. Such a compilation presupposes an extensive library, assiduous reading and a retentive memory, so that whatever Mirfield's defects may be, his knowledge, if not his experience of practical medicine, was on a large scale. As usual, there are a number of charms and remedies taken from folk-lore, but he gave no credence to them. The extracts from the *Breviarium* published by Hartley and Aldridge are, as the authors admit, quite arbitrary: many others equally interesting and revealing could be adduced, though it is doubtful whether they would increase our knowledge to any great extent. Among the sources he used were Hippocrates, Pliny Secundus, Rhases, Avicenna, Mesue, Bartholomew of Salerno, Platearius, Gilbertus Anglicus, Gaddesden, to name but a few. He also wrote a theological work, the *Florarium*. In Chapter 88, *De medicis et eorum medicinis*, he knits together a number of passages from Bernard Gordon, Bruno Longoburgo, William of Saliceto, Lanfranc of Milan, the *Regimen Salernitanum* and many other sources, including Canon Law, in such a skilful way that the unwary reader might be misled into thinking that his strictures on physicians are his own and refer to his own times. In fact, they have other connections; but Mirfield's dexterity in weaving the sources together without any hiatus shows that he fully grasped the material with which he was dealing.

Another compiler was William Holme, a Franciscan friar and a Doctor of Medicine. His book, entitled *De simplicibus medicinis*, written with the same purpose in view as the *Breviarium Bartholomaei*, consisted of remedies, taken from the twelve most renowned medical writers, Haly Abbas, Avicenna, Rhases, and so on, listed alphabetically with the sicknesses they were intended to cure. This compilation eventually came into the hands of Thomas Deynman, physician to Henry VII and his mother Margaret Beaufort, and later warden of the hospital of St Mary Bethlehem, and through him passed to Peterhouse, Cambridge. This book was used extensively by John Argentine, Provost of King's College, Cambridge, in his own compilation, *Loci communes seu liber de morbis et medicinis*, written about a century later. So here we have a typical example of that continual process of borrowing, not merely from original sources, but also from compilations on secondary sources, which paralysed all effort to widen the horizons of medicine or to discover something new and interesting.

It may have been this stagnation in medical ideas and the consequent diminution of the aura that surrounded the physicians which prompted laymen, who by this time could gain instruction in medical matters by recourse to the vernacular texts, to practise medicine themselves. For quite suddenly, as it seemed, the physicians began to feel that their social status was endangered and they took steps to defend their standing and reputation. In 1421 they petitioned Parliament to prevent anyone from practising medicine unless he had graduated in 'the scoles of Fisyck withynne some Universitee, that is to say, he be Bacheler or Doctour of Fisyck, havyng lettres testimonyalx sufficientz of one of those degrees of the Universitee in whiche he toke his degree, under peyne of long imprisonment and paynge xl *li*. to the kyng: and that no Woman use the practyse of Fisyck undre the same payne.' Parliament asked that a warrant should be sent to all the sheriffs throughout the country and to all practitioners with an order that those who intended to practise medicine should present themselves at a University, submit to an examination and receive a degree. Those who failed to pass would be automatically disqualified from medical practice. This petition came to nothing for it was soon realised that the number of qualified practitioners was totally inadequate to deal with the population. Two years later a more limited proposal was put before the Mayor and aldermen of London, this time addressed by both physicians and surgeons: they asked authority to establish a joint college 'for the better education and control of physicians and surgeons practising within the City and its liberties'. The five petitioners were Gilbert Kymer, physician to Duke Humphrey, John Somerset, later physician to Henry VI, Thomas Southwell, Thomas Morstede, the celebrated surgeon, and John Harwe, a Master of the craft of Surgery. It was their intention to acquire premises containing at least three rooms, 'wherof oon be ichaired and desked for redyng and disputacions in Philosophye and in medicyns; And that other for congregacions, eleccions and Counseils of all Phisicians practisyng Phisyck ... And the thrid for congregacions, eleccions and Counseils of all Cirurgeans wirkyng in ye crafte of Cirurgy.' The purpose of the scheme was to establish proper examinations for all physicians and surgeons, to supervise all cases of sickness and injury, to bring negligent practitioners before the Mayor's courts, to regulate fees and to provide free treatment for the poor. Two apothecaries were assigned to the Commonalty of physicians and surgeons, whose responsibility it was to examine druggists' shops, destroy bad medicines and charge offenders before the mayor and aldermen. When one considers that a scheme such as this had been in force in Italian cities like Lucca for almost two centuries, the backwardness of the English medical profession can be realised. It is also noticeable that one of the main interests of the physicians seems to have been disputations in philosophy, a remote and utterly useless means for advancing the interests of clinical medicine.

The ordinances suggested to the authorities in London were successfully passed, but the so-called College was short-lived. It dealt with one case in 1424 when William Forest sued John Harwe for malpractice in treating a wounded hand which resulted in permanent loss of the use of the right thumb. Gilbert Kymer, assisted by three other physicians and four surgeons, including Thomas Morstede and William Bradwardine, heard the evidence and acquitted Harwe and his assistants of malfeisance; but the reasons they adduced sound rather obscurantist: 'They declared that any defect, mutilation, or disfigurement of the hand was due either to the Constellations aforesaid (*i.e.*, Aquarius and Gemini) or some defect of the patient or of the original nature of the wound.'

In this same year (though the manuscript dates it 1404) Kymer wrote for Duke Humphrey, his patron, a *Dietarium de sanitatis custodia*. In it he styles himself 'Professor of Medicine, Master of Arts and Philosophy and Bachelor of Law', a reminder that medicine was not his sole interest. At this time he was Head of the London doctors and was later to become Chancellor of Oxford University on two separate occasions. The *Dietarium* furnishes a perfect example of the intellectual level of the physicians at this time. Like Bredon, Mirfield and the rest, he was content to be a compiler and he says at the beginning 'I shall say nothing which has not been approved by authority, reason and experience', meaning the authority, reason and experience of others. Though the treatise is well written in good Latin, 'laying aside my mother tongue', and is logically drawn up, it contains not one iota of information which could not be found in the *Regimen Salernitanum* written more than two centuries earlier. It comprises twenty-six chapters, dealing with the praise of health, choice of air, quality of food and drink, the quantity, order and time when they are to be taken, the choice of bread, pottages, meats, fish, eggs, milk foods, fruits, condiments and drinks, *de usu coitus*, the use of exercise, sleep and rest, the moderating of the passions of anger and the rest, the best medicines to be employed, and a final chapter on the service of God. Though he quotes Hippocrates, Galen, Constantine, Isaac Judaeus and Roger Bacon, it is obvious that his immediate source was the *Secretum secretorum* attributed to Aristotle and that he was borrowing from the same source as the vernacular poems and treatises which were current among the bulk of the literate population. Whilst his tract is interesting in its revelation of certain social habits, such as dining at midnight and later, and rising at ten or eleven o'clock in the morning, and refers to spices and fruits that were evidently imported from as far off as Corinth and Damascus, it points to a poverty of ideas among the medical men in high places that, judging by their academic qualifications, is scarcely credible.

Whether or not the competence of English physicians was doubted by the moneyed and noble patrons who employed them is not clear. But precisely at this time a number of foreign physicians found their way to the English Court. There were at least four attached to the household of Henry IV: David de Nigarellis from Lucca, Elias di Sabbato, a Jew from Italy, Lorenço Gomes from Portugal and Peter of Alcobaça, also a Portuguese. Another, Demetrius de Cerno, a Greek, was personal physician to Lucia Visconti, Countess of Kent. Even Duke Humphrey, who still retained Kymer in his service, recommended an Italian, John de Signorellis, to his nephew, Henry VI. Of these Elias di Sabbato was the most interesting. He came from Fermo and for his medical expertise had been granted, contrary to all custom, the citizenship of Rome by Pope Innocent VII. His renown at the papal court evidently reached the ears of Henry IV through ambassadorial channels, and when the King, who had been suffering with an unknown ailment for a year, found no English physician to cure him, he invited Elias to come to England. Elias, who moved in exalted company, was not easily lured. Since he was a religious man who regularly celebrated the 'minyen' (a service that could not be held without the presence of ten companions), he stipulated, before accepting the invitation, that his safe conduct should extend to ten other Jews, their horses, equipage and goods, and that he should be free to exercise his art without hindrance wherever he went. The King was evidently so impressed by what he had heard of Elias' qualifications that on 27 December, 1410, he willingly granted his request. Elias came to England, served the royal court for one year (with what success is not known), returned to Italy and eventually became physician to Martin V and other Popes. His successor, David de Nigarellis, from Lucca, was equally welcome at the English court: he stayed about the same time, returned to his native land and, after a most fruitful life in the practice of medicine, left behind a large and impressive library. The influx of foreign physicians continued throughout the century, and whilst their English counterparts could produce nothing but strings of remedies, copied from the most extraordinary sources, or comment on the texts produced some six centuries before (like John Cokkys' *Thesaurus gratie*), the Italians, Frisians, Spaniards, French and Portuguese enjoyed universal favour.

The obvious superiority of the foreign physicians may have been one of the reasons which prompted Englishmen to travel abroad to enlarge their knowledge and experience. In the twelfth century Salerno had been the goal; in the thirteenth it was Paris and Montpellier, with Bologna taking third place; in the period of which we are speaking, Padua was the attraction. The first to take his medical degrees there was William Hattecliffe, one of the royal physicians, who went to Padua in 1446 and proceeded M.D. the following year. He was followed by John Argentine in 1465 and John Free, sometime after 1471. In 1477 John Clerke obtained his medical degree there and finally Linacre, of whom we shall speak later, was admitted M.D. in 1496. But none of them stayed on Italian soil long enough to become imbued with the new enthusiasm, the new ideas and new methods that made Italian medicine so progressive. They were satisfied with possessing an academic title which lifted them above their fellows socially, but did nothing to transform their approach to the treatment of disease. When Henry VI, after a long illness, lapsed into insanity, his medical advisers, Hattecliffe among them, could think of nothing more efficacious to bring about relief than electuaries, potions, waters, sirups, clysters, fomentations and the clap-trap that had paraded under the guise of rational treatment for centuries.

But about the middle of the century a change in the attitude of physicians became discernible. Whereas, before, most of them had treated surgery and surgeons with disdain, they now began to take an interest in this branch of medicine, and though it may have been a purely theoretical and academic interest, few of them failed to gather on their shelves the classic texts of Roger Frugardi, Bruno, William of Salicet, Lanfranc, de Mondeville, and Guy de Chauliac. Some of them even had the more modern Italian books on surgery such as Azzeleta of Bologna. The translation of these texts into the vernacular may have been due to some of them, but there is no certainty on this score. The craft of surgery was evidently becoming respectable and in one particular instance William Hobbes, who had taken his M.D. at Oxford and Cambridge, made surgery his sole occupation.

The reason for this was that from 1415 onwards (in fact, during the whole of the Hundred Years War), the importance of the surgeons had risen enormously. The demand for skilled men who could dress the wounds of the soldiers during and after battle grew steadily, and the effectiveness of their treatment, their ingenuity in devising new instruments for dealing with awkward and unusual cases and their proven ability to keep an army in the field raised them in public esteem. The physicians, on the other hand, had been practically useless; with all their potions and remedies, their *regimen*, their knowledge of medical texts, they had been powerless to stop the spread of dysentery at Harfleur and the consequent paralysis of the army. When, on 24 April, 1430, Henry V set sail for

France, a petition was made in Council for the provision of four surgeons, answerable to the royal surgeon, William Stalworth, to accompany him at wages of sixpence a day, and a grant of £20 was made for sundry medicines, instruments, dressings and other things necessary for surgical treatment. This was following the tradition of the earlier expedition of 1415 when Thomas Morstede had taken twelve surgeons with him supported by two carts carrying medical supplies for the army. On these expeditions the surgeons had ample opportunity of increasing their knowledge and manual dexterity, of experimenting with various kinds of powders, plasters and fomentations for closing wounds, and of inventing means for extracting arrows, knitting fractured limbs and so on: their craft needed courage, boldness, decisive action and swift treatment. A mere acquaintance with books was not sufficient and, in fact, book knowledge had sometimes to be discarded in favour of experience. So it came about that surgery, long the Cinderella of medical science, took an honoured place, and its practitioners stood high in the royal and public regard. Men like Morstede, Bradwardine and Harwe were rewarded for their services; and whilst physicians, for the most part clerics, were raised to bishoprics, deaneries, chancellorships and posts of academic distinction, the surgeons, like Morstede and Bradwardine, were honoured with knighthoods. Between the wars surgery still made progress, for the apprentice system ensured that the knowledge of the master was passed on to his pupil. In some cases we can trace the handing over of this accumulated experience for three or four generations: Thomas Dayron taught Thomas Morstede and at his death bequeathed to him his two best books on physic and surgery, namely Avicenna and Bruno Longoburgo; Morstede, in his turn, had two pupils, to one of whom he bequeathed his own composition *The Fayre Book of Surgery* together with all his surgical instruments; both these latter assistants pursued the craft of surgery, though not attaining the eminence of their master. The same can be said for the Dagville family of surgeons, and for the Ashbornes.

One interesting point about the surgeons was their independence of the apothecaries. Whereas the physicians merely prescribed and gave advice, leaving the apothecary to compound the drugs and administer them (a practice that was eventually to lead to the apothecaries assuming medical practice), the surgeons appear not only to have made up their own medicines, but to have possessed their own drug shops. This is shown in their wills. John Dagville left his son all the medicines in his two shops, besides several surgical books in Latin and English together with his instruments in silver, laton and iron, whilst Thomas Colard bequeathed to his son copies of Gaddesden and Constantine, all his instruments of iron and steel 'and alle gumys and powderes and suche things as longyth to surgery with ther vessells that be in ii furneys poots' and 'four basyns of laton of them that hangyth in the schoppe and vi of them that hangyth without'.

Though there were a few foreign surgeons practising in England, they did not compete so successfully with the natives as did the foreign physicians. A stricter control appears to have been exercised over their activities and as they did not possess university degrees, which empowered the holders to practise wherever they wished without let or hindrance, they had to submit to the normal examination imposed on all surgeons. This examination was carried out both by accredited physicians and surgeons and towards the end of the fifteenth century the licence was granted either by the Chancellor in the university towns or by the bishop of the diocese in other places. A typical licence of this kind survives, granted by the Bishop of London:

Richard, by grace and sufferance of God Bishopp of London, to all true christian peple . . . Whereas in avoydyng dyvers and grevous hurts and Jeopardyes which in the Realme of Englande dayly happen by the presumptuouse unponnyshed boldnesse of unkonnyng surgions, it was of late holsomly and politikely enacted that it shuld nott be lefull to any person within the saide Realme to occupy the crafte of Surgery, Except he were first examined and admitted by certayn persons to whom that power and auctorite by the said statute is committed. We therefore to whom the same auctorite be the saide ordenance is gevyn within the cite of London and vii myles in circute abowte the same, with the assistance of John Smyth doctour of physike, called unto us for the singular trust that we have in hym in this behalff, callyng also unto us iiij experte persons in the faculte of surgery after the tenor of the saide arte, that is to say John

Johnson, John Pyerson, William Litygo and Thomas Sybson of London, Barbour surgeons by us aforetyme admytted to Surgerye be the saide arte have diligently examenyd William Ashewell of London, Barbour Surgeon, and have fownde the same William Ashewell ryght hable and sufficient to occupye the saide crafte of surgery and as one hable and sufficient there unto we have hym approvyed and admittyd.

A certain amount of jealousy was engendered when surgeons of foreign origin were taken into the royal service, for they were not bound by the same regulations. The Wardens of the Surgeons Guild did not brook this with equanimity and one of them at least, Thomas Rosse, persisted in demanding that Balthazar Guercio, a native of Italy and surgeon to Queen Katherine of Aragon, should prove his competence before an approved committee. The King intervened and published an injunction restraining Rosse from pursuing Guercio until he had proved that surgery was a handicraft. Rosse, instancing Chiron at the siege of Troy, stated that surgery was an 'operatio manualis'. It consisted:

in staunchyng of blod, serchyng of wounds with irons and other instruments, in cutting of the sculle in due proporcion to the pellicules of the brayne with instruments of iron, cowchyng of catharacts, cutting of apostumes, burnyng of cankers and other lyke, settyng in of joynts and byndyng them with ligatures, lettyng of blod, drawyng of tethe, with other suche lyke, which restyth onely in manual operation, princypally with the hands of the werkman.

He said that surgery bears the same relation to physic as carpentry to geometry – a revealing remark. And after quoting a great number of authors, Gerard, Avicenna, Theodoric, Gilbertus Anglicus, Guy de Chauliac, Rhases and St Jerome, he concluded:

These authors be authorised by our Mother Holy Church, in whom as yet I more believe, for theyr trouth and theyr long contyneuance, and in the olde and auncyent probable customes aboveseid, then in any newe autors, as alyens or straungers denying the auctours aboveseid, and forsakyng the trowth and the doctours of their owne facultie, entendyng in this realme of England custumally to contynewe and dwell withoute lycense, law or contradiccyon, ayenst right and the due order of justice.

This shows, besides a resentment against the intrusion of foreigners into English surgery, a strong literary conservatism which disliked the introduction of new texts and perhaps new methods. But the time was ripe for a fresh wind to blow through the mists and fogs of English medical education. It was to come from the very place and people that Rosse was criticizing, and was to come through the most conservative members of the medical profession, the physicians.

In 1487 Thomas Linacre, Fellow of All Souls College, Oxford, accompanied William Sellyng on a diplomatic mission to Italy. He did not return to England for ten, possibly twelve years, and during that time he studied under some of the greatest scholars of the Renaissance, under Poliziano and Chalcondylas at Florence, Ermolao Barbaro at Rome and Leonico Tomeo at Padua. Though most of these studies were classical, medicine was one of his preoccupations and at Padua in 1496 he took his doctorate in it. There can be no doubt that his contacts with academic life in Italy impressed on him the low standards operating in his native country. But it was the editions of Greek texts of both Hippocrates and Galen which first opened his eyes to what he considered might herald a new era in medical knowledge and, though he did not expect that all medical men would learn Greek, as he had done, he thought that new translations would reveal much that had been unknown to previous generations. He gave himself to this task and published six translations of Galen, about one tenth of the total volume of Galen's works. Little did he suspect that, by perpetuating the authority of Galen, he was encouraging the very stagnation he purposed to remove. This work, however, combined with his other writings and translations, gave him great authority among his compeers and when, about 1509, he became physician to the Court of Henry VIII he was able to exert it for the betterment of medical education and practice. We may see, perhaps, the extent of his influence in the Act of Parliament passed two years later forbidding the practice of physic and surgery within the city of London and the suburbs for seven miles around to any man who had not been examined, approved and admitted by the Bishop of London, a practice common to the cities of Italy since the thirteenth century. For some undefinable reason this enactment was found insufficient to curb abuses, or there may have been an attempt to break away from the imposition of ecclesiastical authority. After seven years another petition was submitted for the establishment of a College of learned and weighty men practising medicine, who should, within the same limits as those designated in the previous Act of Parliament, supervise the practice of physic, punish quacks and charlatans and grant licences only to those who were fully qualified. The prime movers in this affair were John Chambre, Thomas Linacre and Ferdinand de Vittoria, three royal physicians, together with Nicholas Halsewell, John Francis and Robert Yaxley. Though Linacre is named second in this list, there is little doubt that his influence was greatest, for though he was attached to the Court he was also personal physician to Cardinal Wolsey, then at the highest point in his career. Wolsey, significantly, was the last signatory to this petition for the foundation of a College.

When the charter of foundation was granted, Linacre gave the front part of his house as a meeting place for the members of the College and endowed it with part of his library, the rest of it being given to Merton College, Oxford. No provisions for teaching were contained in the charter granted to the College, for its purpose was to guard and enchance the ethical and intellectual standards of the medical profession, and particularly of its own members. But Linacre took other steps to advance medical education by establishing both at Oxford and Cambridge three lectureships in medicine, which have survived up to the present day. This was the last beneficial act he was able to perform for the medical profession, for he died eight days later on 20 October, 1524. Not long afterwards the College of Physicians enlarged its scope by extending its functions to teaching also, but much time elapsed before the spirit of its founder, in some ways progressive, enlightened, and zealous for the highest standards, succeeded in animating later generations to explore the wider horizons of scientific medicine.

Bibliography

This is not strictly a bibliography, but a list of books in English for those who may wish to supplement the information given in the various chapters.

CHAPTER I
ANGLO-SAXON MEDICINE

J. F. Payne: *English Medicine in Anglo-Saxon Times*, Oxford, 1904.
Singer, C. and Gratton, J. H. G.: *Anglo-Saxon Medicine and Magic, Illustrated Especially from the Semi-pagan Text Lacnunga*, London, 1962.

CHAPTER II
ARAB MEDICINE

D. Campbell: *Arabian Medicine*, London, 1926.
C. Elwood: *Medicine in Persia*, Clio Medica no. xiv, New York, 1934.

CHAPTER III
SALERNO

L. C. Mackinney: *Early Medieval Medicine*, Baltimore, 1937.
The School of Salernum, trs. by Sir J. Harington, London, 1922.

CHAPTER V
MEDICAL EDUCATION

Hastings Rashdall: *The Universities of Europe in the Middle Ages*, ed. by F. M. Powicke and A. B. Emden, 3 vols., 1958.

CHAPTER VI
GILBERTUS ANGLICUS

H. F. Handerson: *Gilbertus Anglicus. Medicine of the 13th Century*, Cleveland, 1918.

CHAPTER VII
SURGERY

The Surgery of Theodoric of Cervia, trs. by E. Campbell and J. Colton, New York, 1960.
Lanfranc's Science of Cirurgie, Early Eng. Text Soc. 1894, orig. ser. 102.

213

CHAPTER VIII
JOHN GADDESDEN

H. P. Cholmeley: *John of Gaddesden and the Rosa Medicinae*, Oxford, 1912.

CHAPTER IX
ANATOMY

Sidney Young: *The Annals of the Barber Surgeons of London*, London, 1890.

D'Arcy Power: *Arderne's Treatises of Fistula in Ano*, Early Engl. Text Soc. 1910, orig. ser. 139.

CHAPTER XII
HYGIENE

Lawrence Wright: *Clean and Decent*, London, 1960.

CHAPTER XIII
EPIDEMICS

C. Creighton: *History of Epidemics in Great Britain*, London, 1891–94.

D. Singer and A. Anderson: *Catalogue of Latin and Vernacular Plague Texts*, Paris, 1950.

CHAPTER XIV
HOSPITALS

Rotha M. Clay: *The Medieval Hospitals of England*, London, 1909.

CHAPTER XVI
THE FINAL PHASE

P. Horton-Smith Hartley and H. R. Aldridge: *Johannes de Mirfield, His Life and Works*, Cambridge, 1936.

C. D. O'Malley: *English Medical Humanists*, Kansas, 1965.

G. Clark: *A History of the Royal College of Physicians*, Oxford, 1964–66.

Index

215

Theodorus Priscianus, 15, 19, 73, 80
Theophilus, 43, 46, 48, 66, 73, 121
Thibaut of Étampes, 53
Thomas Aquinas, 73, 189
Thomas of Eblesburne, 83
Thomas of Essex, 84
Thomas de Goldington, 178
Thomas of Weseham, 195
Toledo, 35, 40
Tomeo, Leonico, 210
Toulouse, 121
Touraine, 149
Tours, 46, 51–2, 55
Trajan, emperor, 13
Trevisa, 186
Trivet, Nicholas, 82
Trotula, 41, 81
Tyngewick, Nicholas, 107–9

Urso of Calabria, 43, 48

Valentine, Saint, 131
Valencia, bishop of, 98
Valeys, Robert, 199
Venice, 92, 118, 119
Verona, 92, 99
Victor III, pope, 39
Vincent des Bois, 177
Vindician, 15, 19, 53
Visconti, Lucia, Countess of Kent, 204
Visconti, family, 101
Vitus, Saint, 162
Vivarium, abbey, 13

Walafrid Strabo, 66

Walter, Hubert, archbishop of Canterbury, 72
Walter Agilon, 111, 121
Walter, brother, 181
Waltham, abbey, 46
Warin, abbot of Saint Albans, 47
Wearmouth, abbey, 17
Werferth, bishop of Worcester, 17
Werwulf, priest, 17
Westminster, abbey, 46, 149, 151
Wighard, archbishop elect of Canterbury, 10
Wight, William, 152
Wilfrid, Saint, 181
William I, king of England, 46
William I, king of Sicily, 58
William II, king of Sicily, 58
William of Brescia, 100
William of Champeaux, 64
William de Congenis, 93–5, 97, 113, 118
William of Fécamp, 84
William de Saliceto, 99–101, 102, 117, 134, 140, 191, 201, 206
William de Somiris (Sumere), 102
Willibrord, Saint, 16, 163
Winchelsey, archbishop of Canterbury, 101
Withington, Edward, 75
Wolsey, Thomas, cardinal, 147, 211
Worcester, priory, 153, 179
Wulfstan, bishop of London, 22
Wurzburg, 17

Xenocrates, 21

Yaxley, Robert, 211
Yonge, James, 189
York, 11, 17, 23, 156